The Open University

GTA1

Symmetry

This publication forms part of an Open University course. Details of this and other Open University courses can be obtained from the Student Registration and Enquiry Service, The Open University, PO Box 197, Milton Keynes, MK7 6BJ, United Kingdom: tel. +44 (0)870 300 6090, e-mail general-enquiries@open.ac.uk

Alternatively, you may visit the Open University website at http://www.open.ac.uk where you can learn more about the wide range of courses and packs offered at all levels by The Open University.

To purchase a selection of Open University course materials, visit http://www.ouw.co.uk, or contact Open University Worldwide, Michael Young Building, Walton Hall, Milton Keynes, MK7 6AA, United Kingdom, for a brochure: tel. +44 (0)1908 858793, fax +44 (0)1908 858787, e-mail ouw-customer-services@open.ac.uk

The Open University, Walton Hall, Milton Keynes, MK7 6AA.

First published 2006. Reprinted with amendments 2007.

Edited, designed and typeset by The Open University, using the Open University TeX System.

Printed and bound in the United Kingdom by Hobbs the Printers Limited, Brunel Road, Totton, Hampshire SO40 3WX.

ISBN 0 7492 0215 7

1.2

Contents

Introduction to Group Theory Block A

This block is the first of two concerning a branch of mathematics known as group theory. It introduces the basic ideas leading up to a simple, yet powerful result known as *Lagrange's Theorem*, which underpins much of the development of the subject. The second block, Group Theory Block B, investigates the theory further.

Groups appear in many branches of pure mathematics. They also occur naturally in other fields, such as chemistry and physics.

We introduce the idea of a group by using the geometric concept of *symmetry*. Symmetry occurs in nature in many ways; for example, the human form is (outwardly) symmetric, as are many biological, chemical and geological forms.

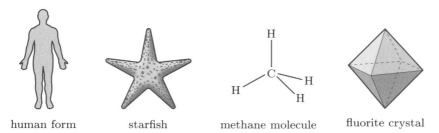

human form   starfish   methane molecule   fluorite crystal

We investigate symmetry groups, groups arising out of addition and multiplication (including modular arithmetic) and permutation groups. We use tables, known as *group tables*, to represent small groups, and discover special types of groups, including *cyclic groups* and *Abelian groups*. We find subsets of groups which are groups in their own right, and which we call *subgroups*. We then show that each subgroup can be used to define a partition of the group into *cosets*. These cosets play a central role in the proof of Lagrange's Theorem.

Although one of the goals of this block is to establish some abstract theory, our approach throughout will be to introduce and illustrate the ideas using concrete examples.

Introduction

In this unit we use the geometric concept of symmetry to introduce some of the basic ideas of group theory, including *group tables*, and the four properties, or *axioms*, that define a group.

In Section 1 we discuss intuitive ideas of symmetry for a two-dimensional figure, and define the set of *symmetries* of such a figure. We then view these symmetries as functions that combine under composition, and show that the resulting structure has properties known as *closure*, *identity*, *inverses* and *associativity*. We use these properties to define a *group* in Section 3.

In Section 2 we develop an algebraic notation for recording symmetries, and demonstrate how to use the notation to calculate *composites* of symmetries and the *inverse* of a symmetry.

Section 3 is the audio section. We begin by defining the terms *group*, *Abelian group* and *order of a group*. We then demonstrate how to check the group axioms, and we extend the examples of groups that we use to include groups of numbers—the modular arithmetics, the integers and the real numbers.

In Section 4 we prove that some of the properties of the groups appearing earlier in the unit are, in fact, general properties, shared by all groups. In particular, we prove that in any group the identity element is unique, and that each element has a unique inverse.

Finally, in Section 5, the video section, we extend our ideas of symmetry to three dimensions and consider, in particular, the regular (Platonic) solids.

Study guide

The main content of this unit is in the first three sections, all of which are quite substantial. You should study these sections thoroughly and in order.

By contrast, the details of the proofs in Section 4 are less important, and you should not spend a lot of time struggling with them if you find them difficult to follow. However, you need to know the results, particularly the uniqueness results; you also need to be able to use the results, so you should tackle the exercises in this section.

The video section is fairly free-standing, although before watching it you should be familiar with the group axioms, given at the beginning of Section 3.

This is quite a substantial unit and you may find that the study time needed for it is slightly greater than for an average unit.

1   Symmetry in $\mathbb{R}^2$

After working through this section, you should be able to:

(a) explain what is meant by a *symmetry* of a plane figure;

(b) specify symmetries of a bounded plane figure as rotations or reflections;

(c) describe some properties of the set of symmetries of a plane figure;

(d) explain the difference between *direct* and *indirect* symmetries.

1.1   Intuitive ideas of symmetry

We begin by considering some intuitive ideas of symmetry. Probably you think of symmetry in terms of figures like a heart-shape, which has two 'equal and opposite' halves, or like a capital N, which can be thought of as being made up of two equal pieces. Mathematically, we can express these ideas in terms of transformations which leave the figure as a whole looking the same.

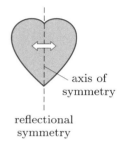

axis of symmetry

reflectional symmetry

The heart-shape, for example, has *reflectional symmetry* because a reflection in the *axis of symmetry* leaves the figure looking the same. Similarly, the letter N has *rotational symmetry* because a half-turn about the centre leaves the figure looking the same. Rotational symmetry need not involve a half-turn: in other circumstances it may involve a quarter-turn or a third of a turn, for example.

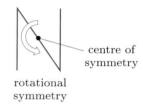

centre of symmetry

rotational symmetry

Rotations and reflections can be used to describe symmetry because they are transformations of the plane that preserve distances between points. That is, the distance between any two points is the same as the distance between their images. Such transformations act on a figure like the heart-shape without distorting its size or shape.

We can apply our ideas of symmetry to any plane figure, but we shall choose many of our examples from the regular polygons.

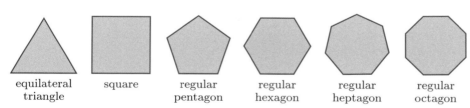

equilateral triangle   square   regular pentagon   regular hexagon   regular heptagon   regular octagon

In order to develop our ideas of symmetry, we look at the square.

We consider the square to be a subset of the plane, with its four vertices located at definite positions in $\mathbb{R}^2$. This means that the size of the square, its location in the plane and its orientation are completely determined. We keep track of the configuration of the square by putting distinguishing marks at two of the corners.

initial position

We define a *symmetry* of the square to be a transformation of the plane that maps the square to itself and preserves distances between points. The technical name for a function that preserves distances is an *isometry*. The only isometries of the plane are translations, rotations and reflections, and combinations of these. Any non-trivial translation alters the location of the square in the plane and so cannot be a symmetry of the square.

The *trivial translation* is the translation through zero distance; all other translations are *non-trivial*.

We therefore consider only rotations and reflections as potential symmetries of the square.

To specify a rotational symmetry of a figure, we need to give a point which is the *centre of rotation* and the *angle* through which the figure is turned. Note that we always measure angles anticlockwise, and interpret negative angles as clockwise. The angle $\pi/2$, for example, means an anticlockwise rotation through $\pi/2$ radians, whereas $-\pi/2$ means a clockwise rotation through $\pi/2$ radians.

The square has four rotational symmetries: rotations about the centre of the square through 0, $\pi/2$, π and $3\pi/2$ radians (anticlockwise) all map the square to itself. A rotation through 0 radians is equivalent to not moving the square, and we call this the *identity symmetry*.

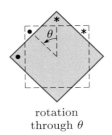

rotation
through θ

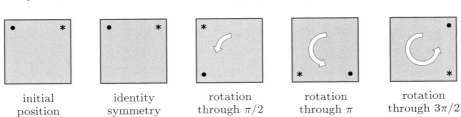

| initial position | identity symmetry | rotation through $\pi/2$ | rotation through π | rotation through $3\pi/2$ |

A rotation through 2π radians returns the square to its original position and so is the same symmetry as the identity symmetry. Similarly, a rotation through $5\pi/2$ radians is the same symmetry as a rotation through $\pi/2$ radians because its overall effect on the square is the same. A rotation through $-\pi/2$ radians is the same symmetry as a rotation through $3\pi/2$ radians because a rotation through $\pi/2$ radians clockwise has the same effect on the square as a rotation through $3\pi/2$ radians anticlockwise.

To specify a reflectional symmetry of a figure, we need to give the *axis of symmetry* in which the figure is reflected. The square has four such axes of symmetry: a vertical axis, a horizontal axis and two diagonal axes. So it has four reflectional symmetries.

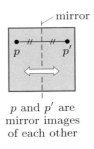

mirror

p and p' are mirror images of each other

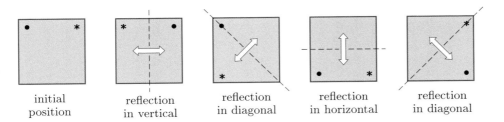

| initial position | reflection in vertical | reflection in diagonal | reflection in horizontal | reflection in diagonal |

This completes the set of symmetries of the square. It contains eight elements: the identity, three non-trivial rotations and four reflections.

Exercise 1.1 For each of the following figures, describe the set of symmetries by drawing diagrams similar to those given above for the square.

A *trivial rotation* is a rotation through any multiple (positive, negative or zero) of 2π; all other rotations are *non-trivial*.

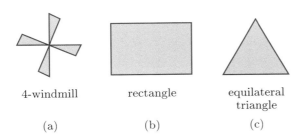

| 4-windmill | rectangle | equilateral triangle |
| (a) | (b) | (c) |

1.2 Formalising ideas of symmetry

Having explored some intuitive ideas of symmetry, we now make some formal definitions, starting with the definition of a figure.

Definition   A **plane figure** is any subset of the plane $\mathbb{R}^2$.

Next we define a symmetry of a plane figure.

Definitions   An **isometry** of the plane is a function $f : \mathbb{R}^2 \longrightarrow \mathbb{R}^2$ that preserves distances; that is, for all $x, y \in \mathbb{R}^2$, the distance between $f(x)$ and $f(y)$ is the same as the distance between x and y.

A **symmetry** of a figure F is an isometry mapping F to itself—that is, an isometry $f : \mathbb{R}^2 \longrightarrow \mathbb{R}^2$ such that $f(F) = F$.

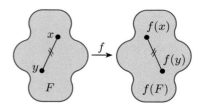

Remark   It is a consequence of these definitions that a symmetry is a one-one and onto function. We prove this later on page 12.

A translation is an isometry; but for a bounded figure such as a square, a non-trivial translation is not a symmetry because it does not map the figure onto itself. The isometries that interest us as potential symmetries of bounded plane figures are the following.

The **identity**: equivalent to doing nothing to a figure.
A **rotation**: specified by a centre and an angle of rotation.
A **reflection**: specified by a line—the axis of symmetry.
A **combination** of the above isometries.

We need to be able to describe formally the situation when two symmetries are the same. For example, we have seen that a rotation through 2π radians has the same effect on a plane figure as the identity symmetry.

Definition   Two symmetries f and g of a figure F are **equal** if they have the same effect on F; that is, $f(x) = g(x)$ for all $x \in F$.

One-one functions and *onto functions* are defined in Unit I2.

A *bounded figure* in $\mathbb{R}^2$ is a figure that can be surrounded by a circle (of finite radius).

Sometimes the identity is called the *trivial symmetry*. It can be regarded as a zero rotation or a zero translation.

1.3 Symmetries of a plane figure

In this subsection we describe some properties that are shared by all sets of symmetries of plane figures.

We denote the set of all symmetries of a plane figure F by $S(F)$. For every figure F, we include the identity symmetry, usually denoted by e. So every figure F has a non-empty set of symmetries.

The elements of $S(F)$ are distance-preserving functions $f : \mathbb{R}^2 \longrightarrow \mathbb{R}^2$ such that $f(F) = F$. So we can form the composite of any two elements f and g in $S(F)$ to obtain the function $g \circ f : \mathbb{R}^2 \longrightarrow \mathbb{R}^2$.

Let $f, g \in S(F)$. Since f and g both map F to itself, so must $g \circ f$; and since f and g both preserve distance, so must $g \circ f$. Hence $g \circ f \in S(F)$. We describe this situation by saying that the set $S(F)$ is *closed* under composition of functions.

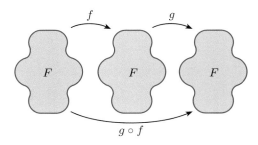

Remember that $g \circ f$ means f first, then g.

Property 1.1   The set of symmetries $S(F)$ of a plane figure F is closed under composition of functions; that is, for all $f, g \in S(F)$,

$$g \circ f \in S(F).$$

We shall look at some examples of composition in $S(\square)$, the set of symmetries of the square. The following diagram shows our standard labelling for the elements of $S(\square)$ which we described in Subsection 1.1. The identity symmetry (not shown) is denoted by e.

We read $S(\square)$ as 'S-square'.

Many texts use r_θ, q_ϕ notation to describe the symmetries in $S(\square)$, where:

$$a = r_{\pi/2}, \ b = r_\pi, \ c = r_{3\pi/2},$$
$$r = q_{\pi/2}, \ s = q_{3\pi/4},$$
$$t = q_0, \ u = q_{\pi/4}.$$

We explain this notation in Subsection 1.4, where we use it to describe the symmetries of a disc.

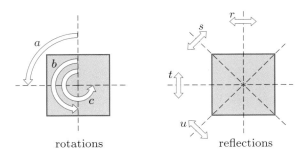

rotations   reflections

Remember that the axes are fixed in the plane; so, for example, r means 'reflect in the vertical axis of symmetry, regardless of any symmetries already carried out'. You may find it useful to remember the above notation: the rotations are a, b and c in order of the rotation angle; the reflections are r, s, t and u starting from the vertical axis of symmetry and working anticlockwise. We adopt a similar convention for some of the other regular polygons.

Example 1.1   Find the following composites of symmetries of the square:

$$a \circ t, \quad t \circ a.$$

Solution   We draw pictures with symbols in two corners of the square, as in Subsection 1.1, to keep track of the composition of the symmetries. You may like to cut out a square from paper to model the square in the plane. To physically model a reflection of the square, you have to lift it out of the plane, turn it over and then replace it in the plane. You will therefore need to mark the two symbols on both sides of the paper.

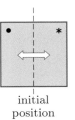

initial position   reflected square

The following diagram shows the effect of $a \circ t$; that is, first t and then a.

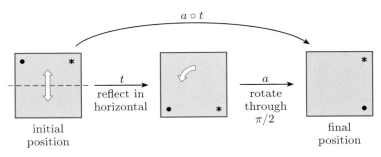

Comparing the initial and final positions, we see that the effect of $a \circ t$ is to reflect the square in the diagonal from bottom left to top right. This is the symmetry that we have called u, so

$a \circ t = u.$

We summarise this information in a single diagram as follows.

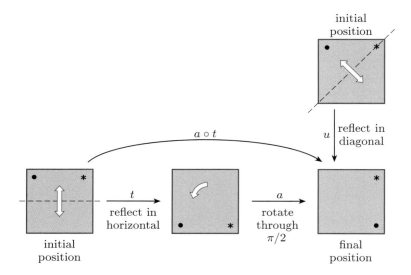

Similarly, we find the composite $t \circ a$.

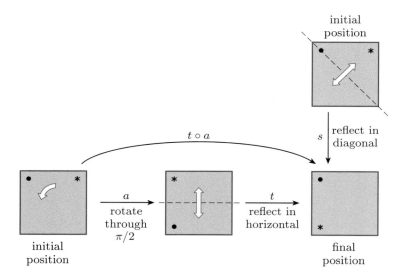

Comparing the initial and final positions, we see that the effect of $t \circ a$ is to reflect the square in the diagonal from top left to bottom right. This is the symmetry that we have called s, so

$t \circ a = s.$ ■

Notice that $t \circ a \neq a \circ t.$

Exercise 1.2   With the notation given above, find the following composites of symmetries of the square:

$b \circ c, \quad s \circ s, \quad t \circ s.$

Example 1.1 and Exercise 1.2 illustrate a number of properties of composition of symmetries of a figure F.

1. Order of composition is important.

   For example, in Example 1.1 we saw that
   $$a \circ t = u \quad \text{but} \quad t \circ a = s.$$

   In general, if $f, g \in S(F)$, then $g \circ f$ may not be equal to $f \circ g$. That is, in general, composition of symmetries is not commutative.

2. Composition of rotations and reflections follows a standard pattern.

   For example, in $S(\square)$,
   $$b \circ c = a,$$
   $$a \circ t = u,$$
   $$t \circ a = s,$$
   $$t \circ s = a.$$

   rotation $\circ$ rotation $=$ rotation
   rotation $\circ$ reflection $=$ reflection
   reflection $\circ$ rotation $=$ reflection
   reflection $\circ$ reflection $=$ rotation

   We can summarise this information in a table.

$\circ$	rotation	reflection
rotation	rotation	reflection
reflection	reflection	rotation

   Note that any bounded plane figure can have at most one centre of non-trivial rotation, and that any axis of symmetry will pass through this centre.

3. Composing a reflection with itself gives the identity.

   For example, in $S(\square)$,
   $$r \circ r = e, \quad s \circ s = e, \quad t \circ t = e, \quad u \circ u = e.$$

   This should be no surprise! If you reflect twice in the same axis you get back to where you started.

   Exercise 1.3 The following diagrams show our standard labelling for the symmetries of a 4-windmill and a rectangle. We denote these sets of symmetries by $S(\text{WIND})$ and $S(\square)$, respectively. In each case, the identity symmetry (not shown) is denoted by e. We shall usually assume this without further comment.

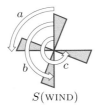

$S(\text{WIND})$

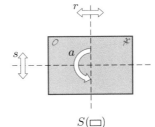

$S(\square)$

(a) For the 4-windmill, find the following composites of symmetries:
$$a \circ a, \quad a \circ b, \quad a \circ c.$$

(b) For the rectangle, find the following composites of symmetries:
$$a \circ r, \quad a \circ s, \quad r \circ s.$$

Exercise 1.4   The following diagram shows our standard labelling for the symmetries of an equilateral triangle. We denote this set of symmetries by $S(\triangle)$.

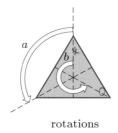   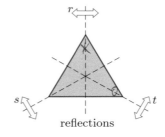

rotations   reflections

The labelling of the reflections here does not follow the convention described on page 9.

Find the following composites of symmetries of the equilateral triangle:

$$a \circ b, \quad a \circ r, \quad s \circ t.$$

At the beginning of this subsection, we stated that any plane figure has at least one symmetry—the identity symmetry—and so $S(F)$, the set of symmetries of a plane figure F, is non-empty. We shall note the existence of an identity as our second property of symmetries; we note also that the identity symmetry e composed with any symmetry $f \in S(F)$, in either order, is simply f.

Property 1.2   The set $S(F)$ contains an **identity symmetry** e such that, for each symmetry $f \in S(F)$,

$$f \circ e = f = e \circ f.$$

We remarked earlier that a symmetry $f : \mathbb{R}^2 \longrightarrow \mathbb{R}^2$ is a one-one and onto function. This is because it is distance preserving. To see that f is one-one, suppose that x and y are any two points of $\mathbb{R}^2$ such that $f(x) = f(y)$. Then the distance between $f(x)$ and $f(y)$ is zero and so the distance between x and y must be zero also. Hence $x = y$, as required.

To see that f is onto, we use the fact that f leaves the size and shape of figures unchanged. In particular any circle centred at the origin O is mapped by f to a circle (of the same radius) centred at $O' = f(O)$. To see how this observation helps, let x' be an element in the codomain $\mathbb{R}^2$ of f. If r is the distance from x' to O', then x' lies on the circle C' of radius r centred at O'. By our observation, C' is the image of the circle C of radius r centred at O, so x' must be the image of some point x on C. Since x' is an arbitrary point of the codomain, f must be onto.

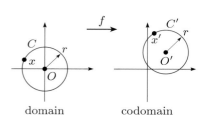

domain   codomain

Because any symmetry $f \in S(F)$ is a one-one and onto function, it must have an inverse function $f^{-1} : \mathbb{R}^2 \longrightarrow \mathbb{R}^2$. Moreover, since f preserves distances and maps F to itself, so must f^{-1}. In other words, f^{-1} is also a symmetry of F, so $f^{-1} \in S(F)$. The composite of f and f^{-1}, in either order, must be the identity symmetry e.

Property 1.3   For each symmetry $f \in S(F)$, there is an **inverse symmetry** $f^{-1} \in S(F)$ such that

$$f \circ f^{-1} = e = f^{-1} \circ f.$$

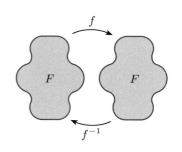

We illustrate this property by looking again at $S(\square)$.

Example 1.2   Find the inverse of each of the elements of $S(\square)$.

Solution   The symmetry a is a rotation through $\pi/2$ about the centre. We should expect the inverse of a to be a rotation through $-\pi/2$; this is the same symmetry as c, a rotation through $3\pi/2$. Composing a and c in either order results in a full turn, which returns each point of the square to its original position. So we have

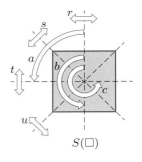

$$a \circ c = e = c \circ a, \qquad (1.1)$$

and we write

$$a^{-1} = c.$$

Equations (1.1) show that a is the inverse of c, so we can write

$$c^{-1} = a.$$

The symmetry b is a rotation through a half-turn, and composing b with itself returns the square to its original position. So

$$b \circ b = e$$

and the symmetry b is its own inverse: $b^{-1} = b$. We describe this situation by saying that b is **self-inverse** or that b is a **self-inverse element**.

In our discussion earlier we remarked that when composing a reflection with itself we obtain the identity, so the elements r, s, t and u in $S(\square)$ are all self-inverse:

$$r^{-1} = r, \quad s^{-1} = s, \quad t^{-1} = t, \quad u^{-1} = u.$$

The element e is unique in $S(\square)$ because it has no effect on the square. Since $e \circ e = e$, it follows that e is its own inverse, so

$$e^{-1} = e.$$

We summarise the results of this example in the following table.

Element	e	a	b	c	r	s	t	u
Inverse	e	c	b	a	r	s	t	u

■

In this case, the two equations corresponding to Property 1.3 are identical.

Exercise 1.5   Draw up a table of inverses for each of the following sets of symmetries.

(a) $S(\text{WIND})$

(b) $S(\square)$

(c) $S(\triangle)$

There is one further important property of composition of symmetries of a figure F, which is not as obvious as those that we have considered so far. This property is called *associativity* and is a general property of composition of functions. The following figure shows two ways of composing three symmetries f, g and h in that order. We can begin with the composite $g \circ f$, and compose that with h on the left as $h \circ (g \circ f)$. Alternatively, we can begin with f, and compose that with the composite $h \circ g$ on the left to form $(h \circ g) \circ f$.

Remember that $g \circ f$ means f first, then g.

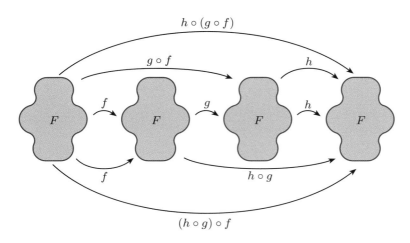

These two approaches give identical results because each one means 'do f first, then g and then h'. Formally, we write

$$h \circ (g \circ f) = (h \circ g) \circ f.$$

In practical terms, associativity means that we may dispense with brackets in writing a composite of three elements: there is no ambiguity in writing $h \circ g \circ f$. It means also that we may group or regroup elements in a large expression to suit our purposes, provided that we do not alter the order in which the elements appear.

For example,
$$\begin{aligned} a \circ b \circ c \circ d &= (a \circ b) \circ (c \circ d) \\ &= a \circ (b \circ c) \circ d \\ &= ((a \circ b) \circ c) \circ d. \end{aligned}$$

Property 1.4 Composition of symmetries is associative; that is, for all $f, g, h \in S(F)$,

$$h \circ (g \circ f) = (h \circ g) \circ f.$$

Subtraction, for example, is not associative:
$$10 - (7 - 3) \neq (10 - 7) - 3.$$

Exercise 1.6 In $S(\square)$, check that

$$a \circ (t \circ a) = (a \circ t) \circ a.$$

In Example 1.1 we found that $a \circ t = u$ and $t \circ a = s$.

Symmetries of a regular n-gon

We close this subsection by generalising our observations about the equilateral triangle and the square to the regular n-gon. A regular n-gon is a polygon with n equal edges and n equal angles, and it has both rotational and reflectional symmetries. For example, an equilateral triangle has six symmetries: three rotations and three reflections. A square has eight symmetries: four rotations and four reflections.

Recall that we may think of the identity symmetry e as a rotation.

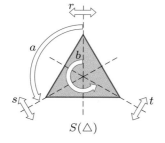

$S(\triangle)$

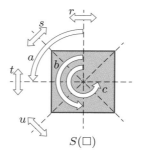

$S(\square)$

In general, a regular n-gon has $2n$ symmetries: n rotations (through multiples of $2\pi/n$) and n reflections in the axes of symmetry through the centre.

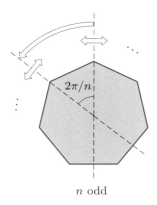 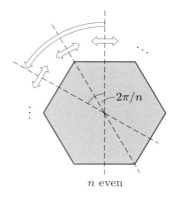

n odd

n even

For odd values of n, each of the n axes of symmetry passes through a vertex and the midpoint of the opposite edge.

For even values of n, there are $\frac{1}{2}n$ axes of symmetry which pass through opposite vertices and $\frac{1}{2}n$ axes of symmetry which pass through the midpoints of opposite edges.

1.4 Symmetries of the disc

A bounded figure that we have not considered yet is the disc. Rotation about the centre through any angle is a symmetry of the disc. Likewise, reflection in any axis through the centre is a symmetry of the disc. Thus the disc has infinitely many rotational and infinitely many reflectional symmetries.

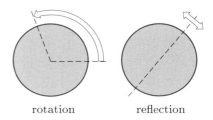

rotation   reflection

We cannot use individual letters to label these symmetries, so we denote a rotation about the centre through an angle θ by r_θ, and a reflection in the axis of symmetry making an angle ϕ with the horizontal axis by q_ϕ.

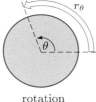 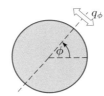

rotation
through θ

reflection in line at
angle ϕ to horizontal

Rotations through θ and $\theta + 2k\pi$, for $k \in \mathbb{Z}$, produce the same effect, so we restrict the angles of rotation to the interval $[0, 2\pi)$. Reflection in the line at an angle ϕ to the horizontal produces the same effect as reflection in the line at an angle $\phi + \pi$ to the horizontal (in fact, it is the same line), so we restrict the angles for axes of symmetry to the interval $[0, \pi)$.

 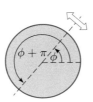

The symmetries of the disc are:

r_θ: rotation through an angle θ about the centre, for
$\theta \in [0, 2\pi)$;

q_ϕ: reflection in the line through the centre at an angle ϕ to
the horizontal (measured anticlockwise), for $\phi \in [0, \pi)$.

15

The identity symmetry e is r_0, the zero rotation. Note that q_0 is reflection in the horizontal axis and is not the identity symmetry.

We denote the set of symmetries of the disc by $S(\bigcirc)$, read as 'S-disc':

$$S(\bigcirc) = \{r_\theta : \theta \in [0, 2\pi)\} \cup \{q_\phi : \phi \in [0, \pi)\}.$$

We can compose these symmetries using pictures similar to those that we used when composing symmetries in $S(\square)$. We keep track of a point on the disc and the orientation of the disc by marking a small arrow pointing anticlockwise at a point on the horizontal axis. For example, consider a rotation through $\pi/2$ followed by a rotation through $\pi/4$.

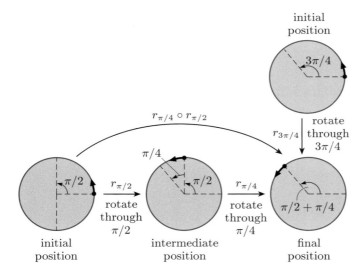

The resulting symmetry is a rotation through $3\pi/4$, and we may write this as

$$r_{\pi/4} \circ r_{\pi/2} = r_{3\pi/4}.$$

Now consider a reflection in the axis making an angle $\pi/2$ with the horizontal axis, followed by a reflection in the axis making an angle $\pi/4$ with the horizontal axis.

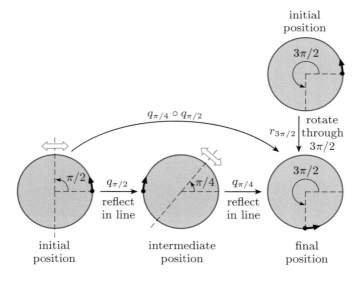

The resulting symmetry is a rotation through an angle $3\pi/2$, and we may write this as

$$q_{\pi/4} \circ q_{\pi/2} = r_{3\pi/2}.$$

As a final example, consider a rotation through an angle $\pi/2$ followed by a reflection in the axis making an angle $\pi/4$ with the horizontal axis. You may expect this composite to be a reflection, and this is indeed the case.

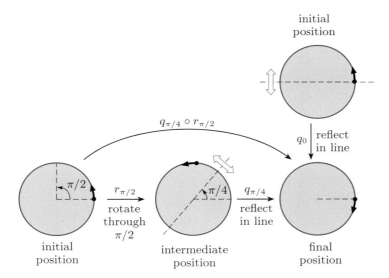

The resulting symmetry is a reflection in the horizontal axis, and we may write this as

$$q_{\pi/4} \circ r_{\pi/2} = q_0.$$

Exercise 1.7   Find the composite $r_{\pi/4} \circ q_{\pi/2}$.

The general formulas for the composition of elements in $S(\bigcirc)$ are summarised in the following table.

$\circ$	r_θ	q_θ
r_ϕ	$r_{(\phi+\theta) \ (\mathrm{mod}\ 2\pi)}$	$q_{(\frac{1}{2}\phi+\theta) \ (\mathrm{mod}\ \pi)}$
q_ϕ	$q_{(\phi-\frac{1}{2}\theta) \ (\mathrm{mod}\ \pi)}$	$r_{2(\phi-\theta) \ (\mathrm{mod}\ 2\pi)}$

For example, q_π followed by $r_{\pi/2}$ results in

$$r_{\pi/2} \circ q_\pi = q_{(\pi/4+\pi) \ (\mathrm{mod}\ \pi)}$$
$$= q_{5\pi/4 \ (\mathrm{mod}\ \pi)}$$
$$= q_{\pi/4}.$$

Rather than derive these general formulas, we ask you to verify each of them in a specific case.

Exercise 1.8   Check that the formulas given in the table hold for the following four examples of composites already found:

$$r_{\pi/4} \circ r_{\pi/2}, \quad q_{\pi/4} \circ q_{\pi/2}, \quad q_{\pi/4} \circ r_{\pi/2}, \quad r_{\pi/4} \circ q_{\pi/2}.$$

1.5 Direct and indirect symmetries

You may have noticed that, in most of the sets of symmetries of plane figures that we have considered, the symmetries are of two sorts: those that we can demonstrate with a model without turning it over, and those for which we need to take the model out of the plane, turn it over and replace it in the plane. In the case of a symmetry group of a bounded plane figure, the former are rotations and the latter are reflections. For example, for $S(\square)$ it is possible to obtain all the reflections by turning the model over and then rotating it. We illustrate this in the following diagram using the reflected model shown in the margin.

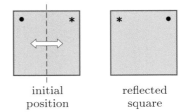

initial position   reflected square

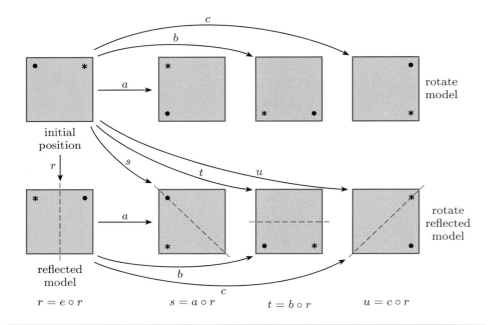

$$r = e \circ r \qquad\qquad s = a \circ r \qquad\qquad t = b \circ r \qquad\qquad u = c \circ r$$

Definition   The symmetries of a plane figure F that we can physically demonstrate without lifting a model out of the plane to turn it over are called **direct** symmetries. We denote the set of direct symmetries of a figure F by $S^+(F)$.

The remaining symmetries are called **indirect** symmetries: they are the symmetries that cannot be demonstrated physically without lifting a model out of the plane, turning it over and then replacing it in the plane.

For example, $S^+(\square) = \{e, a, b, c\}$, the set of rotations.

Remarks

1. Rotations and translations are direct symmetries, whereas reflections are indirect symmetries.

2. The diagram above for the square illustrates a general result. If a figure has indirect symmetries, then they can all be obtained by composing each of the direct symmetries with any one fixed indirect symmetry. There are therefore two possibilities for a finite symmetry group of a plane figure. Either the group has no indirect symmetries, as in $S(\text{WIND})$, or it has as many indirect symmetries as direct symmetries, as in $S(\square)$. In other words, a finite symmetry group of a plane figure comprises either

    *   all direct symmetries, or
    *   half direct symmetries and half indirect symmetries.

3. There is another way to model indirect symmetries that does not involve lifting the figure out of the plane. Here two models are made—the first to represent the figure and the second to represent the reflected figure. Direct symmetries can be demonstrated by rotating the first model and indirect symmetries by rotating the second model. Thus symmetries that can be demonstrated with the first model are direct symmetries and those that require the second model are indirect symmetries.

4. Some unbounded plane figures have indirect symmetries called *glide-reflections*. A **glide-reflection** is a composite of a reflection and a translation. Rotations, reflections, translations and glide-reflections are the only possible symmetries of plane figures. We do not consider glide-reflections further in this course.

Exercise 1.9   Write down the following sets of direct symmetries.

(a) $S^+(\triangle)$ (b) $S^+(\square)$

Draw a diagram for each set (similar to the one for $S(\square)$ given on page 18) to show how the indirect symmetries can be obtained from the direct symmetries by using just one indirect symmetry.

In Subsection 1.3 we gave some results about composites of rotations and reflections. These can be generalised to similar results about direct and indirect symmetries.

direct   ∘ direct   = direct
direct   ∘ indirect = indirect
indirect ∘ direct   = indirect
indirect ∘ indirect = direct

∘	direct	indirect
direct	direct	indirect
indirect	indirect	direct

Further exercises

Exercise 1.10   Describe geometrically the symmetries of each of the following figures.

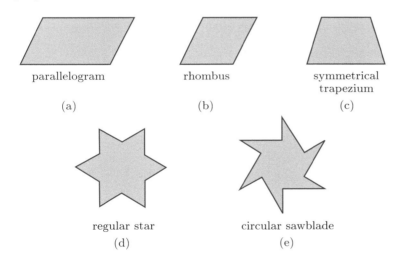

| parallelogram | rhombus | symmetrical trapezium |
| (a) | (b) | (c) |

regular star   circular sawblade
(d)   (e)

Exercise 1.11   The figure shown in the margin is an equilateral curve heptagon. Its symmetries are:

seven anticlockwise rotations: e, a, b, c, d, f and g about the centre through increasing multiples of $2\pi/7$;

seven reflections: r, s, t, u, v, w and x in the axes shown.

Determine the following composites:

$b \circ d, \quad f \circ g, \quad c \circ v, \quad x \circ u.$

Exercise 1.12   Draw up a table of inverses for the symmetries of the equilateral curve heptagon using the notation of Exercise 1.11.

This is the shape of a 50p coin.

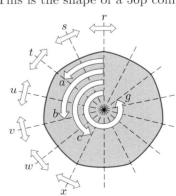

Exercise 1.13   List the direct symmetries of the equilateral curve heptagon using the notation of Exercise 1.11. Show how each of the indirect symmetries can be obtained as the composite of the indirect symmetry w and a direct symmetry.

2   Representing symmetries

After working through this section, you should be able to:

(a) use a *two-line symbol* to represent a symmetry;

(b) describe geometrically the symmetry of a given figure which corresponds to a given two-line symbol;

(c) find the composite of two symmetries given as two-line symbols;

(d) find the inverse of a symmetry given as a two-line symbol;

(e) write down a *Cayley table* for the set of symmetries of a plane figure;

(f) appreciate how certain properties of the set of symmetries of a figure feature in a Cayley table.

2.1   Two-line symbol

So far we have represented symmetries of plane figures by letters, and used diagrams or models to work out composites. This method is illuminating but time consuming. In this section we introduce an algebraic notation which permits us to manipulate and compose symmetries easily, but at the expense of geometric intuition.

We illustrate the notation in terms of the symmetries of a square. In the diagram we have labelled the locations of the vertices of the square with the numbers 1, 2, 3 and 4. In our discussion we consider these numbers as being fixed to the background plane. So the number 1 is always at the top left-hand corner of the square in this example. It does not label the vertex of the square, and so does not move when we apply a symmetry to the square. We use these numbers to record the effect of a symmetry as follows.

We first consider the effect of the symmetry a (rotation through $\pi/2$ about the centre).

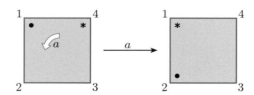

The symmetry a maps the vertices as follows.

shorthand

vertex at location 1 to location 2 $1 \longmapsto 2$
vertex at location 2 to location 3 $2 \longmapsto 3$
vertex at location 3 to location 4 $3 \longmapsto 4$
vertex at location 4 to location 1 $4 \longmapsto 1$

We can think of a as a function mapping the set $\{1, 2, 3, 4\}$ to itself.

$$a : \begin{cases} 1 \longmapsto 2 \\ 2 \longmapsto 3 \\ 3 \longmapsto 4 \\ 4 \longmapsto 1 \end{cases} \quad \text{or} \quad a : \begin{array}{cccc} 1 & 2 & 3 & 4 \\ \downarrow & \downarrow & \downarrow & \downarrow \\ 2 & 3 & 4 & 1 \end{array}$$

Strictly, a symmetry does not act on the numbers 1, 2, 3, 4. We use 1, 2, 3, 4 here as shorthand for 'the vertex of the square at location 1', etc.

We model our new notation for a on the second version, omitting the arrows and enclosing the numbers in parentheses: thus we write

$$a = \begin{pmatrix} 1 & 2 & 3 & 4 \\ 2 & 3 & 4 & 1 \end{pmatrix}.$$

The symmetry r has the following effect.

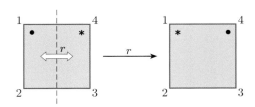

Thus the symmetry r

> interchanges the vertices at locations 1 and 4,
> interchanges the vertices at locations 2 and 3.

So, in our new notation, we write

$$r = \begin{pmatrix} 1 & 2 & 3 & 4 \\ 4 & 3 & 2 & 1 \end{pmatrix}.$$

The identity symmetry e leaves all the vertices at their original locations, so we write

$$e = \begin{pmatrix} 1 & 2 & 3 & 4 \\ 1 & 2 & 3 & 4 \end{pmatrix}.$$

We refer to this notation for recording a symmetry of a plane figure as the *two-line symbol* for the symmetry. To specify a symmetry in this form, we must first give a picture of the figure with labelled locations.

Example 2.1   For the square with vertices at locations 1, 2, 3 and 4, labelled as shown, describe geometrically the symmetry represented by the two-line symbol

$$\begin{pmatrix} 1 & 2 & 3 & 4 \\ 2 & 1 & 4 & 3 \end{pmatrix}.$$

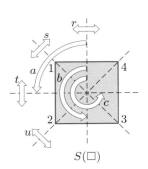

Solution   This two-line symbol represents a symmetry that

> interchanges the vertices at locations 1 and 2,
> interchanges the vertices at locations 3 and 4.

Thus the symmetry has the following effect.

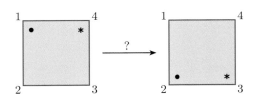

So the two-line symbol represents reflection in the horizontal axis—the symmetry t. ∎

Exercise 2.1 Find the two-line symbols representing the remaining symmetries of the square, namely b, c, s and u, using the labelling of locations given in Example 2.1.

Exercise 2.2 Find the two-line symbols representing each of the four symmetries of the labelled rectangle in the margin. (Do not forget e.)

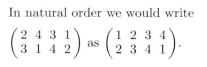

$S(\square)$

There is no universal way of labelling the locations of a plane figure, so the two-line symbols depend on the choice of labels. For example, for the square and rectangle above, reflection in the vertical axis is represented by a different two-line symbol in each case because we have used different systems for labelling the locations of the vertices (anticlockwise around the square, but across the top and bottom of the rectangle).

Usually, we try to maintain an anticlockwise labelling of the locations of the vertices, starting at the top left.

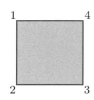

Now we define formally the two-line symbol representing a symmetry of a polygonal figure.

Definition Let f be a symmetry of a polygonal figure F which moves the vertices of the figure F originally at the locations labelled $1, 2, 3, \ldots, n$ to the locations labelled $f(1), f(2), f(3), \ldots, f(n)$, respectively.

The **two-line symbol** representing f is

$$\begin{pmatrix} 1 & 2 & 3 & \ldots & n \\ f(1) & f(2) & f(3) & \ldots & f(n) \end{pmatrix}.$$

We cannot choose $f(1)$, $f(2), \ldots$ arbitrarily here, as f must be a symmetry of F.

Remarks

1. The order of the columns in the symbol is not important, although we often use the natural order to aid recognition. For example, using the location labels as shown, we would normally write the two-line symbols for the eight symmetries of the square as follows.

In natural order we would write

$$\begin{pmatrix} 2 & 4 & 3 & 1 \\ 3 & 1 & 4 & 2 \end{pmatrix} \text{ as } \begin{pmatrix} 1 & 2 & 3 & 4 \\ 2 & 3 & 4 & 1 \end{pmatrix}.$$

rotations		reflections

$$e = \begin{pmatrix} 1 & 2 & 3 & 4 \\ 1 & 2 & 3 & 4 \end{pmatrix} \qquad r = \begin{pmatrix} 1 & 2 & 3 & 4 \\ 4 & 3 & 2 & 1 \end{pmatrix}$$

$$a = \begin{pmatrix} 1 & 2 & 3 & 4 \\ 2 & 3 & 4 & 1 \end{pmatrix} \qquad s = \begin{pmatrix} 1 & 2 & 3 & 4 \\ 1 & 4 & 3 & 2 \end{pmatrix}$$

$$b = \begin{pmatrix} 1 & 2 & 3 & 4 \\ 3 & 4 & 1 & 2 \end{pmatrix} \qquad t = \begin{pmatrix} 1 & 2 & 3 & 4 \\ 2 & 1 & 4 & 3 \end{pmatrix}$$

$$c = \begin{pmatrix} 1 & 2 & 3 & 4 \\ 4 & 1 & 2 & 3 \end{pmatrix} \qquad u = \begin{pmatrix} 1 & 2 & 3 & 4 \\ 3 & 2 & 1 & 4 \end{pmatrix}$$

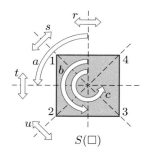

$S(\square)$

2. Not all two-line symbols represent symmetries of a particular figure. For example, with our choice of labelling, $\begin{pmatrix} 1 & 2 & 3 & 4 \\ 1 & 3 & 2 & 4 \end{pmatrix}$ is not a symmetry of the square because there is no symmetry which interchanges the vertices at locations 2 and 3, and leaves fixed the vertices at locations 1 and 4.

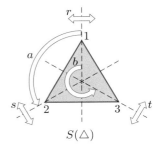

Exercise 2.3   Using the given labelling for the locations of the vertices, write down the two-line symbol for each of the symmetries of the equilateral triangle.

$S(\triangle)$

Exercise 2.4   The following two-line symbols represent symmetries of the hexagon shown. Describe each symmetry geometrically.

(a) $\begin{pmatrix} 1 & 2 & 3 & 4 & 5 & 6 \\ 6 & 5 & 4 & 3 & 2 & 1 \end{pmatrix}$

(b) $\begin{pmatrix} 1 & 2 & 3 & 4 & 5 & 6 \\ 3 & 4 & 5 & 6 & 1 & 2 \end{pmatrix}$

(c) $\begin{pmatrix} 1 & 2 & 3 & 4 & 5 & 6 \\ 3 & 2 & 1 & 6 & 5 & 4 \end{pmatrix}$

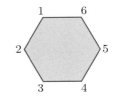

2.2 Composing symmetries

One advantage of the two-line notation for symmetries is that it is easy to form composites. For example, let us form the composite $r \circ a$ of symmetries of the square. We have

$$a = \begin{pmatrix} 1 & 2 & 3 & 4 \\ 2 & 3 & 4 & 1 \end{pmatrix} \quad \text{and} \quad r = \begin{pmatrix} 1 & 2 & 3 & 4 \\ 4 & 3 & 2 & 1 \end{pmatrix},$$

which are shorthand for the functions

$$a : \begin{cases} 1 \longmapsto 2 \\ 2 \longmapsto 3 \\ 3 \longmapsto 4 \\ 4 \longmapsto 1 \end{cases} \quad \text{and} \quad r : \begin{cases} 1 \longmapsto 4 \\ 2 \longmapsto 3 \\ 3 \longmapsto 2 \\ 4 \longmapsto 1 \end{cases}.$$

So the composite $r \circ a$ is given by

$$\begin{matrix} 1 \longmapsto 2 \longmapsto 3 \\ 2 \longmapsto 3 \longmapsto 2 \\ 3 \longmapsto 4 \longmapsto 1 \\ 4 \longmapsto 1 \longmapsto 4 \\ \quad a \qquad r \end{matrix} \; ; \; \text{that is,} \quad \begin{matrix} 1 \longmapsto 3 \\ 2 \longmapsto 2 \\ 3 \longmapsto 1 \\ 4 \longmapsto 4 \\ \quad r \circ a \end{matrix}.$$

Remember that $r \circ a$ means a first, then r.

Thus the two-line symbol for $r \circ a$ is

$$r \circ a = \begin{pmatrix} 1 & 2 & 3 & 4 \\ 3 & 2 & 1 & 4 \end{pmatrix};$$

this is reflection in the diagonal shown—the symmetry u.

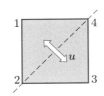

Composing the functions r and a as we did above suggests a method of combining two-line symbols for symmetries without drawing diagrams.

To determine $r \circ a$, the composite of two symmetries r and a written as two-line symbols, we reorder the columns of the symbol for r to make its top line match the order of the bottom line of the symbol for a. We then read off the two-line symbol for the composite $r \circ a$ as the top line of the symbol for a and the bottom line of the symbol for r.

For example, in $S(\square)$,

$$r \circ a = \begin{pmatrix} 1 & 2 & 3 & 4 \\ 4 & 3 & 2 & 1 \end{pmatrix} \circ \begin{pmatrix} 1 & 2 & 3 & 4 \\ 2 & 3 & 4 & 1 \end{pmatrix}$$

$$= \begin{pmatrix} 2 & 3 & 4 & 1 \\ 3 & 2 & 1 & 4 \end{pmatrix} \circ \begin{pmatrix} 1 & 2 & 3 & 4 \\ 2 & 3 & 4 & 1 \end{pmatrix}$$

$$= \begin{pmatrix} 1 & 2 & 3 & 4 \\ 3 & 2 & 1 & 4 \end{pmatrix} = u.$$

After some practice, you may find that you can compose two-line symbols without reordering the columns.

For example, to find $r \circ a$ in $S(\square)$, we first write down

$$r \circ a = \begin{pmatrix} 1 & 2 & 3 & 4 \\ 4 & 3 & 2 & 1 \end{pmatrix} \circ \begin{pmatrix} 1 & 2 & 3 & 4 \\ 2 & 3 & 4 & 1 \end{pmatrix} = \begin{pmatrix} 1 & 2 & 3 & 4 \\ & & & \end{pmatrix}.$$

Then we find the entries of the bottom row in turn.

Now a sends 1 to 2 and r sends 2 to 3, so the composite sends 1 to 3:

$$r \circ a = \begin{pmatrix} 1 & 2 & 3 & 4 \\ 4 & 3 & 2 & 1 \end{pmatrix} \circ \begin{pmatrix} 1 & 2 & 3 & 4 \\ 2 & 3 & 4 & 1 \end{pmatrix} = \begin{pmatrix} 1 & 2 & 3 & 4 \\ 3 & & & \end{pmatrix}.$$

Also a sends 2 to 3 and r sends 3 to 2, so the composite sends 2 to 2:

$$r \circ a = \begin{pmatrix} 1 & 2 & 3 & 4 \\ 4 & 3 & 2 & 1 \end{pmatrix} \circ \begin{pmatrix} 1 & 2 & 3 & 4 \\ 2 & 3 & 4 & 1 \end{pmatrix} = \begin{pmatrix} 1 & 2 & 3 & 4 \\ 3 & 2 & & \end{pmatrix}.$$

The final two entries are found in the same way: a sends 3 to 4 and r sends 4 to 1, so the composite sends 3 to 1; a sends 4 to 1 and r sends 1 to 4, so the composite sends 4 to 4:

$$r \circ a = \begin{pmatrix} 1 & 2 & 3 & 4 \\ 4 & 3 & 2 & 1 \end{pmatrix} \circ \begin{pmatrix} 1 & 2 & 3 & 4 \\ 2 & 3 & 4 & 1 \end{pmatrix} = \begin{pmatrix} 1 & 2 & 3 & 4 \\ 3 & 2 & 1 & 4 \end{pmatrix}.$$

As we have seen already, the order of composition is important. For example,

$$a \circ r = \begin{pmatrix} 1 & 2 & 3 & 4 \\ 2 & 3 & 4 & 1 \end{pmatrix} \circ \begin{pmatrix} 1 & 2 & 3 & 4 \\ 4 & 3 & 2 & 1 \end{pmatrix} = \begin{pmatrix} 1 & 2 & 3 & 4 \\ 1 & 4 & 3 & 2 \end{pmatrix} = s,$$

so

$$r \circ a \neq a \circ r.$$

Exercise 2.5 Using the two-line symbols for the symmetries of the equilateral triangle found in Exercise 2.3, find the following composites:

$$a \circ a, \quad b \circ s, \quad s \circ b, \quad t \circ s.$$

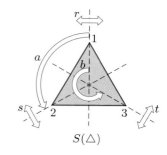

$S(\triangle)$

2.3 Finding the inverse of a symmetry

We saw in Section 1 that every symmetry has an inverse which 'undoes' the effect of the symmetry. There is an easy way to write down the inverse of a symmetry given by a two-line symbol. Let us consider again the symmetry a of the square:

$$a = \begin{pmatrix} 1 & 2 & 3 & 4 \\ 2 & 3 & 4 & 1 \end{pmatrix}.$$

Property 1.3

This is shorthand for the function

$$a : \begin{cases} 1 \longmapsto 2 \\ 2 \longmapsto 3 \\ 3 \longmapsto 4 \\ 4 \longmapsto 1 \end{cases} \quad \text{with inverse} \quad a^{-1} : \begin{cases} 2 \longmapsto 1 \\ 3 \longmapsto 2 \\ 4 \longmapsto 3 \\ 1 \longmapsto 4 \end{cases},$$

The inverse of a function is obtained by reversing the arrows of the function.

so

$$a^{-1} = \begin{pmatrix} 2 & 3 & 4 & 1 \\ 1 & 2 & 3 & 4 \end{pmatrix} = c.$$

Reversing the arrows in the mapping a is equivalent to reading the two-line symbol for a from the bottom to the top. In other words, to find the inverse of a, we turn the two-line symbol upside down. Reordering the columns in the symbol into the natural order is optional but it may make the inverse easier to recognise.

For example,

$$a = \begin{pmatrix} 1 & 2 & 3 & 4 \\ 2 & 3 & 4 & 1 \end{pmatrix}, \quad \text{so} \quad a^{-1} = \begin{pmatrix} 2 & 3 & 4 & 1 \\ 1 & 2 & 3 & 4 \end{pmatrix} \quad \begin{array}{l} \text{(turn the symbol} \\ \text{upside down).} \end{array}$$

$$= \begin{pmatrix} 1 & 2 & 3 & 4 \\ 4 & 1 & 2 & 3 \end{pmatrix} \quad \begin{array}{l} \text{(reorder the} \\ \text{columns).} \end{array}$$

Exercise 2.6   Find the inverse of each of the following symmetries of a regular hexagon, given as a two-line symbol.

(a) $\begin{pmatrix} 1 & 2 & 3 & 4 & 5 & 6 \\ 5 & 6 & 1 & 2 & 3 & 4 \end{pmatrix}$

(b) $\begin{pmatrix} 1 & 2 & 3 & 4 & 5 & 6 \\ 2 & 1 & 6 & 5 & 4 & 3 \end{pmatrix}$

(c) $\begin{pmatrix} 1 & 2 & 3 & 4 & 5 & 6 \\ 4 & 5 & 6 & 1 & 2 & 3 \end{pmatrix}$

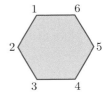

2.4 Cayley tables

Finally in this section, we consider a way of recording composites of symmetries. This is by means of a **Cayley table**. To form the Cayley table for the elements of a set $S(F)$ of symmetries, we list the elements of $S(F)$ across the top and down the left-hand side of a square array.

	e	f	g	$\cdots$	x	y	z
e							
f							
g							
$\vdots$							
x							
y							
z							

The order in which we choose to list the elements is not important, but it is important to use the same ordering across the top and down the side. Normally we put the identity symmetry e first, as shown above. This square array enables us to list every possible composite of pairs of elements in $S(F)$. However, this is practicable only if $S(F)$ is a small set, and is not feasible for $S(\bigcirc)$, which is infinite!

For any two elements x and y of $S(F)$, the composite $x \circ y$ is recorded in the cell in the row labelled x and the column labelled y.

$$
\begin{array}{c|ccc}
 & \cdots & y & \cdots \\
\hline
\vdots & & \vdots & \\
x & \cdots & x \circ y & \cdots \\
\vdots & & \vdots &
\end{array}
$$

Note that x is on the left both in the composite and in the border of the table. Of course, the composite $x \circ y$ is the result of performing first the symmetry y and then the symmetry x.

We have found many of the composites of elements of $S(\square)$ already; for example, $a \circ t = u$, $t \circ a = s$ and $r \circ a = u$. The complete Cayley table for $S(\square)$ is as follows.

$\circ$	e	a	b	c	r	s	t	u
e	e	a	b	c	r	s	t	u
a	a	b	c	e	s	t	u	r
b	b	c	e	a	t	u	r	s
c	c	e	a	b	u	r	s	t
r	r	u	t	s	e	c	b	a
s	s	r	u	t	a	e	c	b
t	t	s	r	u	b	a	e	c
u	u	t	s	r	c	b	a	e

The Cayley table illustrates a number of properties of $S(\square)$ to which we shall refer later.

Closure   No new elements are needed to complete the table because every composite is one of the eight symmetries.

Identity   The row and column labelled by the identity e repeat the borders of the table.

Inverses   The identity e occurs when an element is composed with its inverse, so e appears once in each row and once in each column. Also, e appears symmetrically in the table.

Self-inverse elements   When a self-inverse element is composed with itself, the identity e appears on the leading diagonal of the table. Conversely, when e appears on the leading diagonal, the corresponding element is self-inverse.

Direct and indirect symmetries   We have chosen to list the direct symmetries, e, a, b and c, first, followed by the indirect symmetries, r, s, t and u. This leads to a 'blocking' of the Cayley table, as illustrated below.

Arthur Cayley (1821–1895) was the leading British algebraist of the nineteenth century. He helped to lay the groundwork for the abstract theory of groups and he developed the algebra of matrices and determinants.

The *leading diagonal* or *main diagonal* is the diagonal from top left to bottom right.

○	e	a	b	c	r	s	t	u
e	e	a	b	c	r	s	t	u
a	a	b	c	e	s	t	u	r
b	b	c	e	a	t	u	r	s
c	c	e	a	b	u	r	s	t
r	r	u	t	s	e	c	b	a
s	s	r	u	t	a	e	c	b
t	t	s	r	u	b	a	e	c
u	u	t	s	r	c	b	a	e

○	direct	indirect
direct	direct	indirect
indirect	indirect	direct

We shall see an example of 'blocking' in another Cayley table in Section 5.

Exercise 2.7   Using the two-line symbols from Exercise 2.3 to work out the composites, construct the Cayley table for the symmetries of an equilateral triangle.

You found some of these composites in Exercise 2.5, and also in Exercise 1.4.

Exercise 2.8   Using the labelling of the rectangle shown, construct the Cayley table for $S(\square)$.

Further exercises

Exercise 2.9   Describe geometrically the symmetries of the (non-regular) hexagon shown in the margin. (The sides joining 1 to 6, 2 to 3 and 4 to 5 all have the same length, as do the sides joining 1 to 2, 3 to 4 and 5 to 6.) Write down the two-line symbol for each symmetry.

Exercise 2.10   Write down the two-line symbol for each of the eight symmetries of a square for each of the following labellings.

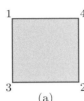
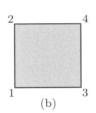

(a)   (b)

$S(\square)$

Exercise 2.11   In the following figure, the labels 1, 2, 3 and 4 refer to the locations of the four edges of the figure (instead of the vertices).

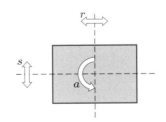

The position of the rectangle may be specified by the locations of the four edges instead of the four vertices. So our definition of two-line symbol still makes sense if we replace vertices by edges.

For this labelling of the rectangle, write down the two-line symbol for each symmetry of the rectangle.

Exercise 2.12   For the labelling of the regular octagon shown in the margin, interpret geometrically each of the following two-line symbols.

(a) $\begin{pmatrix} 1 & 2 & 3 & 4 & 5 & 6 & 7 & 8 \\ 3 & 4 & 5 & 6 & 7 & 8 & 1 & 2 \end{pmatrix}$

(b) $\begin{pmatrix} 1 & 2 & 3 & 4 & 5 & 6 & 7 & 8 \\ 8 & 7 & 6 & 5 & 4 & 3 & 2 & 1 \end{pmatrix}$

(c) $\begin{pmatrix} 1 & 2 & 3 & 4 & 5 & 6 & 7 & 8 \\ 5 & 4 & 3 & 2 & 1 & 8 & 7 & 6 \end{pmatrix}$

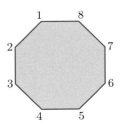

Exercise 2.13   Let

$$x = \begin{pmatrix} 1 & 2 & 3 \\ 3 & 1 & 2 \end{pmatrix} \quad \text{and} \quad y = \begin{pmatrix} 1 & 2 & 3 \\ 3 & 2 & 1 \end{pmatrix}.$$

Find the two-line symbol for each of the following composites:

$$x \circ x, \quad y \circ y, \quad x \circ y, \quad y \circ x.$$

Hence show that

$$(x \circ x) \circ x = e, \quad (x \circ x) \circ y = y \circ x \quad \text{and} \quad y \circ (x \circ x) = x \circ y.$$

3   Group axioms

After working through this section, you should be able to:

(a) explain the meaning of the terms *group*, *Abelian* group and the *order* of a group;

(b) give examples of *finite* groups and *infinite* groups;

(c) determine whether a given set and *binary operation* form a group, by checking the group axioms;

(d) deduce information from a given Cayley table.

3.1 Group properties

In Section 1 we considered the set $S(F)$ of all symmetries of a plane figure F, and we showed that $S(F)$ has certain properties with respect to composition.

1. CLOSURE	The composite of any two symmetries in $S(F)$ is also in $S(F)$.
2. IDENTITY	The set $S(F)$ contains the identity symmetry.
3. INVERSES	Every symmetry of F has an inverse which is also a symmetry of F.
4. ASSOCIATIVITY	Composition of symmetries is associative: composites of three (or more) symmetries in a given order can be written down unambiguously without parentheses.

There are many other circumstances in which we have a set with a means of combining elements which together possess these four properties; for example, sets of real numbers combined under addition or multiplication. We introduce more examples of this kind in the audio section.

The set together with the means of combining two elements, which is called a *binary operation*, are said to form a mathematical structure known as a *group*. For example, the set of symmetries of a figure forms a group under the operation of composition.

To define a group in general, we use the four properties listed above as axioms, and express them in terms of an unspecified binary operation $\circ$ acting on an unspecified set G. Any specific set which has an operation that satisfies these axioms is said to form a group under that operation.

Definition Let G be a set and let $\circ$ be a binary operation defined on G. Then $(G, \circ)$ is a **group** if the following four axioms G1–G4 hold.

G1 CLOSURE For all $g_1, g_2 \in G$,
$$g_1 \circ g_2 \in G.$$

G2 IDENTITY There exists an identity element $e \in G$ such that, for all $g \in G$,
$$g \circ e = g = e \circ g.$$

G3 INVERSES For each $g \in G$, there exists an inverse element $g^{-1} \in G$ such that
$$g \circ g^{-1} = e = g^{-1} \circ g.$$

G4 ASSOCIATIVITY For all $g_1, g_2, g_3 \in G$,
$$g_1 \circ (g_2 \circ g_3) = (g_1 \circ g_2) \circ g_3.$$

Here $\circ$ does not necessarily mean composition of functions.

Example 3.1 Show that the set $S^+(F)$ of direct symmetries of a plane figure F, with the operation of composition, is a group.

Solution We show that the four group axioms hold.

G1 CLOSURE Let $f, g \in S^+(F)$; then f and g are direct symmetries, so $f \circ g$ is also a direct symmetry. Thus,

if $f, g \in S^+(F)$, then $f \circ g \in S^+(F)$,

so $S^+(F)$ is closed under composition.

G2 IDENTITY An identity symmetry is e, the zero rotation, and $e \in S^+(F)$, so $S^+(F)$ contains an identity.

G3 INVERSES Let $f \in S^+(F)$, so f is a direct symmetry; then its inverse must also be a direct symmetry. Thus,

if $f \in S^+(F)$, then $f^{-1} \in S^+(F)$,

so $S^+(F)$ contains an inverse of each of its elements.

G4 ASSOCIATIVITY Composition of symmetries is associative so, in particular, composition of direct symmetries is associative.

Hence $S^+(F)$ satisfies the four group axioms, and so $(S^+(F), \circ)$ is a group. ∎

The property of commutativity is not one of our four basic axioms. A group $(G, \circ)$ that has the additional property of commutativity is given a special name.

Remember that a *direct symmetry* of a plane figure is one that can be demonstrated physically without lifting the model out of the plane.

The word *group* was introduced by the French mathematician Evariste Galois (1811–32) as part of a theory to classify polynomial equations whose solutions can be expressed by a formula involving radicals (nth roots).

Definition Let $(G, \circ)$ be a group that has the additional property that for all $g_1, g_2 \in G$,
$$g_1 \circ g_2 = g_2 \circ g_1.$$

Then $(G, \circ)$ is an **Abelian** group (or **commutative** group).

A group that is not Abelian is called **non-Abelian**.

Abelian groups are named after the Norwegian mathematician Niels Henrik Abel (1802–29), who earlier showed that no formula involving radicals exists for a general quintic equation; formulas for the general cubic and quartic equations had been found in the 16th century.

For example, $(S^+(\square), \circ)$ is an Abelian group, but $(S(\square), \circ)$ is non-Abelian.

In our consideration of symmetry groups we have seen that the underlying set G of a group $(G, \circ)$ may be finite (as in $S(\square)$ and $S(\triangle)$) or infinite (as in $S(\bigcirc)$). If G is a finite set containing exactly n elements, we say that the group $(G, \circ)$ has *order n*. For example, $(S(\square), \circ)$ has order 8, and $(S(\triangle), \circ)$ has order 6. Formally, we make the following definitions.

Definitions   A group $(G, \circ)$ is a **finite** group if G is a finite set; otherwise, G is an **infinite** group.

If G is a finite set with exactly n (distinct) elements, then the group $(G, \circ)$ has **order** n and we denote this by writing

$\quad |G| = n;$

otherwise, $(G, \circ)$ has **infinite order**.

We read $|G|$ as 'the order of G'.

For example, $S(\square)$ contains four elements, so $(S(\square), \circ)$ is a group of order 4, and we write

$\quad |S(\square)| = 4;$

the set $S(\bigcirc)$ is infinite, so $S(\bigcirc)$ is an infinite group and has infinite order.

3.2 Checking group axioms

So far we have considered sets of symmetries of plane figures. These give a large number of examples of groups, many of which are finite. In the audio section we consider how the group axioms apply (or do not apply) in other situations.

Another source of examples of groups is *modular arithmetic*.

Modular arithmetic is discussed in Unit I3.

For example, in arithmetic modulo 4 we work with the set $\mathbb{Z}_4 = \{0, 1, 2, 3\}$ and the operations $+_4$ and $\times_4$, where we take the remainder on division by 4 (that is, discard multiples of 4) after forming the ordinary sum or product. The Cayley tables for these two operations are as follows.

$+_4$	0	1	2	3
0	0	1	2	3
1	1	2	3	0
2	2	3	0	1
3	3	0	1	2

$\times_4$	0	1	2	3
0	0	0	0	0
1	0	1	2	3
2	0	2	0	2
3	0	3	2	1

For example,
$$3 +_4 2 \,(= 5) = 1,$$
$$3 \times_4 2 \,(= 6) = 2.$$

In general, for a and b in

$\quad \mathbb{Z}_n = \{0, 1, 2, \ldots, n-1\},$

the operations $+_n$ and $\times_n$ are defined by

$\quad a +_n b =$ is the remainder of $a + b$ on division by n,

$\quad a \times_n b =$ is the remainder of $a \times b$ on division by n.

You will meet groups based on modular arithmetic in the second half of this subsection.

Listen to the audio as you work through the frames.

Audio

1. Definition of a group

$(G, \circ)$ is a **group** if axioms G1–G4 hold:

G1 CLOSURE   For all $g_1, g_2 \in G$,
$$g_1 \circ g_2 \in G.$$

G2 IDENTITY   There exists an **identity** $e \in G$ such that, for all $g \in G$,
$$g \circ e = g = e \circ g.$$

[cloud: e is unique]

G3 INVERSES   For each $g \in G$, there exists an **inverse** $g^{-1} \in G$ such that
$$g \circ g^{-1} = e = g^{-1} \circ g.$$

[cloud: g^{-1} is unique]

G4 ASSOCIATIVITY   For all $g_1, g_2, g_3 \in G$,
$$g_1 \circ (g_2 \circ g_3) = (g_1 \circ g_2) \circ g_3.$$

2. Strategy 3.1 To determine whether $(G, \circ)$ is a group

To show that $(G, \circ)$ IS a group, show that EACH of G1, G2, G3, G4 HOLDS:

[cloud: check CLOSURE] [cloud: check IDENTITY] [cloud: check INVERSES] [cloud: justify ASSOCIATIVITY]

To show that $(G, \circ)$ IS NOT a group, show that ANY ONE of G1, G2, G3, G4 FAILS:

[cloud: find $x, y \in G$ with $x \circ y \notin G$] OR [cloud: show there's no identity in G] OR [cloud: find ONE element with no inverse in G] OR [cloud: find $x, y, z \in G$ with $x \circ (y \circ z) \neq (x \circ y) \circ z$]

3. Is $(\mathbb{Z}, +)$ a group?

$\mathbb{Z} = \{\ldots, -2, -1, 0, 1, 2, \ldots\}$

G1 CLOSURE   For all $m, n \in \mathbb{Z}$,
$m + n \in \mathbb{Z}$.

G2 IDENTITY   For all $n \in \mathbb{Z}$,
$n + 0 = n = 0 + n$,
and $0 \in \mathbb{Z}$, so identity is 0.

G3 INVERSES   For each $n \in \mathbb{Z}$,
$n + (-n) = 0 = (-n) + n$,
and $-n \in \mathbb{Z}$, so inverse of n is $-n$.

G4 ASSOCIATIVITY   Addition of integers is associative.

Hence $(\mathbb{Z}, +)$ is a group.

4. Is $(\mathbb{R}, \times)$ a group?

closed ✓   1 is identity ✓

$x \times \frac{1}{x} = 1 = \frac{1}{x} \times x$

so inverse of x is $\frac{1}{x}$ for $x \neq 0$.

BUT 0 has no inverse in $\mathbb{R}$.

G3 FAILS

Hence $(\mathbb{R}, \times)$ is not a group.

5. Is $(\mathbb{R}^*, \times)$ a group?

$\mathbb{R}^* = \mathbb{R} - \{0\}$

G1 CLOSURE   For all $x, y \in \mathbb{R}^*$, $x \neq 0$, $y \neq 0$,
so $xy \neq 0$, so $x \times y \in \mathbb{R}^*$.

G2 IDENTITY   For all $x \in \mathbb{R}^*$,
$x \times 1 = x = 1 \times x$,
and $1 \in \mathbb{R}^*$, so identity is 1.

G3 INVERSES   For each $x \in \mathbb{R}^*$, $x \neq 0$, and
$x \times \frac{1}{x} = 1 = \frac{1}{x} \times x$ $\left(\frac{1}{x} \neq 0\right)$
and $\frac{1}{x} \in \mathbb{R}^*$, so inverse of x is $\frac{1}{x}$.

G4 ASSOCIATIVITY   Multiplication of real nos. is associative.

Hence $(\mathbb{R}^*, \times)$ is a group.

6. Exercise 3.1

$\mathbb{Q}$ is set of rationals

Determine which of the following are groups:

(a) $(\mathbb{R}, +)$;

(b) $(\mathbb{Q}, \times)$;

(c) $(\mathbb{Q}^*, \times)$, where $\mathbb{Q}^* = \mathbb{Q} - \{0\}$.

8. Checking G4: does $x \circ (y \circ z) = (x \circ y) \circ z$ for all $x, y, z \in G$?

(i) **subtraction is not associative on** $\mathbb{R}$.

Consider $6, 4, 1 \in \mathbb{R}$:

LHS $6 - (4-1) = 6 - 3 = 3$ $\Big\}$ not equal, so $-$ is

RHS $(6-4) - 1 = 2 - 1 = 1$ $\Big\}$ not associative on $\mathbb{R}$.

G4 FAILS

(ii) $\circ$ **is associative on** $\mathbb{R}$**, where** $x \circ y = x + y + xy$.

Consider $x, y, z \in \mathbb{R}$:

LHS $x \circ (y \circ z) = x \circ (y + z + yz)$
$$= x + (y+z+yz) + x(y+z+yz)$$
$$= x + y + z + yz + xy + xz + xyz$$
$$= x + y + z + xy + xz + yz + xyz; \qquad (1)$$

RHS $(x \circ y) \circ z = (x+y+xy) \circ z$
$$= (x+y+xy) + z + (x+y+xy)z$$
$$= x + y + xy + z + xz + yz + xyz$$
$$= x + y + z + xy + xz + yz + xyz. \qquad (2)$$

(1) and (2) are equal, so, for all $x, y, z \in \mathbb{R}$,
$$x \circ (y \circ z) = (x \circ y) \circ z,$$
so $\circ$ is associative on $\mathbb{R}$.

G4 HOLDS

---

7. Showing that $(G, \circ)$ is NOT a group

(i) $(G = \{\text{odd integers}\}, +)$

G1 CLOSURE

$odd + odd = even$;

specifically, 3 and $5 \in G$, but

$3 + 5 = 8 \notin G$,

so G is not closed under $+$.

G1 FAILS

(ii) $(G = \{\text{even integers}\}, \times)$

closed ✓

G2 IDENTITY

There is no element $e \in G$ such that

$2 \times e = 2$, because $1 \notin G$,

so there is no identity in G.

G2 FAILS

(iii) $(\mathbb{Z}^+, \times)$

closed ✓ *1 is identity ✓*

G3 INVERSES

There is no element $n \in \mathbb{Z}^+$ such that

$2 \times n = 1$, because $\frac{1}{2} \notin \mathbb{Z}^+$,

so 2 has no inverse in $\mathbb{Z}^+$.

G3 FAILS

9. Is $(\mathbb{R}, o)$ a group, where $x \, o \, y = x + y + xy$?

G1 CLOSURE   For all $x, y \in \mathbb{R}$,

$$x \, o \, y = x + y + xy \in \mathbb{R},$$

so $\mathbb{R}$ is closed under o.

(G1 HOLDS)

G2 IDENTITY   We need element $e \in \mathbb{R}$ such that, for all $x \in \mathbb{R}$,

$$x \, o \, e = x + e + xe = x,$$

that is, $e + xe = 0.$

Take $e = 0$; then $e \in \mathbb{R}$ and $x + e + xe = x.$

Also, $e \, o \, x = e + x + ex = x,$

so identity is 0.

(G2 HOLDS)

G3 INVERSES   For each $x \in \mathbb{R}$, we need inverse $y \in \mathbb{R}$ such that

$$x \, o \, y = e,$$

that is, $x + y + xy = 0.$

Solve for y: $y(1+x) = -x,$

so $y = \dfrac{-x}{1+x}$, provided $x \neq -1.$

BUT -1 has no inverse.

(G3 FAILS)

Hence $(\mathbb{R}, o)$ is not a group.

10. Exercises 3.2, 3.3 and 3.4

3.2   Use Strategy 2.1 in Frame 2 to determine which of the following are groups:

(a) $(\mathbb{Z}, \times)$;

(b) $(\mathbb{Z}, -)$;

(c) $(G = \{\text{odd integers}\}, \times)$;

(d) $(2\pi\mathbb{Z}, +)$, where $2\pi\mathbb{Z} = \{2\pi k : k \in \mathbb{Z}\}$;

(e) $(\mathbb{R}, o)$, where $x \, o \, y = x - y - 1.$

3.3   Determine whether each of the following operations o is associative on $\mathbb{R}$:

(a) $x \, o \, y = x + y - xy$;

(b) $x \, o \, y = x - y + xy.$

3.4   (Harder) Show that $(\mathbb{R} - \{-1\}, o)$ is a group, where $x \, o \, y = x + y + xy.$

(Use Frames 8, 9 Watch closure!)

11. Is $(\mathbb{Z}_4, +_4)$ a group?

discard multiples of 4

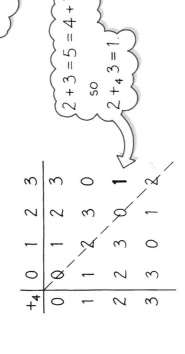

$2 + 3 = 5 = 4 + 1$

so

$2 +_4 3 = 1$.

$+_4$	0	1	2	3
0	0	1	2	3
1	1	2	3	0
2	2	3	0	1
3	3	0	1	2

G1 CLOSURE   No new elements occur in body of table, so $\mathbb{Z}_4$ is closed under $+_4$.

G2 IDENTITY   Row 1 shows that

$0 +_4 x = x$, for each $x \in \mathbb{Z}_4$.

Column 1 shows that

$x +_4 0 = x$, for each $x \in \mathbb{Z}_4$.

Hence identity is 0.

G3 INVERSES   From the table,

$0 +_4 0 = 0$ and $2 +_4 2 = 0$,

so 0 and 2 are self-inverse;

$1 +_4 3 = 0 = 3 +_4 1$,

so 1 and 3 are inverses of each other.

G4 ASSOCIATIVITY $+_4$ is associative.

Hence $(\mathbb{Z}_4, +_4)$ is a group.

12. Is $(\mathbb{Z}_4, \times_4)$ a group?

G3
FAILS

$2 \times 3 = 6 = 4 + 2$

so

$2 \times_4 3 = 2$.

$\times_4$	0	1	2	3
0	0	0	0	0
1	0	1	2	3
2	0	2	0	**2**
3	0	3	2	1

closed ✓   1 is identity ✓

G3 INVERSES   There is no 1 in column labelled 0, so there is no element $x \in \mathbb{Z}_4$ with

$x \times_4 0 = 1$.

Thus 0 has no inverse.

Hence $(\mathbb{Z}_4, \times_4)$ is not a group.

13. Exercise 3.5

Determine which of the following are groups:

(a) $(\mathbb{Z}_5, +_5)$;

(b) $(\mathbb{Z}_5, \times_5)$;

(c) $(\mathbb{Z}_5^*, \times_5)$, where $\mathbb{Z}_5^* = \{1, 2, 3, 4\}$.

14. Information deducible from CAYLEY table

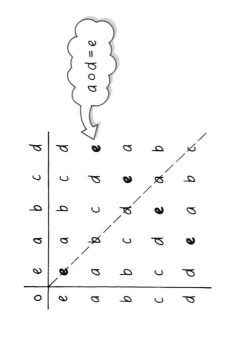

o	e	a	b	c	d
e	e	a	b	c	d
a	a	b	c	d	e
b	b	c	d	e	a
c	c	d	e	a	b
d	d	e	a	b	c

(cloud) $a \circ d = e$

G1 CLOSURE   No new elements occur in body of table, so G is closed under o.

G2 IDENTITY   Row 1 shows that
$$e \circ x = x \text{ for each } x \in G.$$
Column 1 shows that
$$x \circ e = x \text{ for each } x \in G.$$
} Hence identity is e.

G3 INVERSES   From the table, $e^{-1} = e$ and
$$a \circ d = e = d \circ a$$
so $a^{-1} = d$ and $d^{-1} = a$.
Similarly, $b^{-1} = c$ and $c^{-1} = b$.

(cloud) G4 ASSOCIATIVITY not obvious from table

In fact, the table IS a group table.

15. Important properties of GROUP tables

In a GROUP table,
- the identity e must appear symmetrically,
- each element occurs exactly once in each row AND once in each column.

WARNING   A Cayley table with above properties is not necessarily a group table:

o	e	a	b	c	d
e	e	a	b	c	d
a	a	e	c	d	b
b	b	d	e	a	c
c	c	b	d	e	a
d	d	c	a	b	e

- e appears symmetrically
- each element appears once in each row and once in each column

(cloud) G4 FAILS

BUT $b \circ (c \circ d) = b \circ a = d$
$(b \circ c) \circ d = a \circ d = b$ } not the same.

Hence the above table IS NOT a group table.

Post-audio exercises

Exercise 3.6   In each of the following cases, write out a Cayley table and use it to determine whether the given set and binary operation form a group:

(a) $(\mathbb{Z}_6, +_6)$;   (b) $(\mathbb{Z}_6, \times_6)$;

(c) $(\mathbb{Z}_7^*, \times_7)$, where $\mathbb{Z}_7^* = \mathbb{Z}_7 - \{0\}$;   (d) $(\{1, -1\}, \times)$.

Exercise 3.7   Show that $(\mathbb{Q}^+, \circ)$ is a group, where $\mathbb{Q}^+$ is the set of positive rationals and $\circ$ is defined by $a \circ b = \frac{1}{2}ab$.

In this subsection we have seen that the sets $\mathbb{Q}$ and $\mathbb{R}$ are groups with respect to addition and that the sets $\mathbb{Q}^*$ and $\mathbb{R}^*$ are groups with respect to multiplication. The set $\mathbb{C}$ of complex numbers behaves similarly; it is straightforward to show that both $(\mathbb{C}, +)$ and $(\mathbb{C}^*, \times)$ are groups.

You are asked to show that $(\mathbb{C}, +)$ is a group in Exercise 3.8.

3.3 Comments on group axioms

In this section we comment briefly on each of the group axioms.

G1 CLOSURE   For all $g_1, g_2 \in G$,
$$g_1 \circ g_2 \in G.$$

This property is usually easy to check. However, it is essential to check all the details; for example, in $(\mathbb{R}^*, \times)$ it is necessary to check that the product of any two elements is a *non-zero* real number.

G2 IDENTITY   There exists an identity element $e \in G$ such that, for all $g \in G$,
$$g \circ e = g = e \circ g.$$

We have commented already that the identity in a group is unique; we shall prove this result in the next section. In many situations the identity element is obvious and can be identified immediately.

You may quote the following results without further justification.

For composition of functions, the identity is $x \longmapsto x$.

For addition of real and complex numbers, the identity is 0.

For multiplication of numbers, the identity is 1.

G3 INVERSES   For each $g \in G$, there exists an inverse element $g^{-1} \in G$ such that
$$g \circ g^{-1} = e = g^{-1} \circ g.$$

Within a group, the inverse of each element is unique. We shall prove this result in the next section.

You may quote the following results without further justification.

> For composition of functions, the inverse of the function f is the inverse function f^{-1}.

f^{-1} exists when f is one-one.

> For addition of real and complex numbers, the inverse of x is $-x$.

> For multiplication of numbers, real and complex, the inverse of x is $x^{-1} = 1/x$, provided that $x \neq 0$.

G4 ASSOCIATIVITY   For all $g_1, g_2, g_3 \in G$,
$$g_1 \circ (g_2 \circ g_3) = (g_1 \circ g_2) \circ g_3.$$

The following operations are associative and may be quoted as such:

> composition of functions;

> addition of real and complex numbers, modular addition;

> multiplication of real and complex numbers, modular multiplication.

Although the associative property is stated in terms of three elements, it allows us to write down a composite of any finite number of elements without ambiguity. For example, for four elements a, b, c, d and an associative operation $\circ$, an expression such as $a \circ b \circ c \circ d$ is unambiguous. We need not consider the order in which the compositions are carried out, but the order in which the four elements appear must be maintained. We may write

This can be proved formally by induction, but we do not do so here.

$$
\begin{aligned}
a \circ b \circ c \circ d &= (a \circ b) \circ (c \circ d) \\
&= a \circ (b \circ (c \circ d)) \\
&= a \circ ((b \circ c) \circ d) \\
&= (a \circ (b \circ c)) \circ d \\
&\ \ \vdots
\end{aligned}
$$

Further exercises

Exercise 3.8   Show that $(\mathbb{C}, +)$ is a group.

Exercise 3.9   Show that $(2\mathbb{Z}, +)$ is a group where $2\mathbb{Z}$ is the set of even integers $2\mathbb{Z} = \{2k : k \in \mathbb{Z}\}$.

Exercise 3.10   Let $G = \{2^k : k \in \mathbb{Z}\}$. Show that $(G, \times)$ is a group.

Exercise 3.11   Show that each of the following sets, with the binary operation given, is a group.

(a) $(\{1, 3, 5, 7\}, \times_8)$ (b) $(\{1, 2, 4, 7, 8, 11, 13, 14\}, \times_{15})$

(c) $(\{1, 4, 11, 14\}, \times_{15})$ (d) $(\{0, 2, 4, 6, 8\}, +_{10})$

Exercise 3.12   For each of the following sets, with the binary operation given, decide whether it is a group and justify your answer.

(a) $(\mathbb{Z}_9^*, \times_9)$ (b) $(\mathbb{Z}_9, +_9)$ (c) $(\mathbb{Z}_{11}^*, \times_{11})$

$\mathbb{Z}_n^* = \{1, 2, 3, \ldots, n - 1\}$.

4   Proofs in group theory

After working through this section, you should be able to:

(a) understand that the identity in a group is unique;

(b) understand that each element in a group has a unique inverse;

(c) recognise how the uniqueness properties can be proved from the group axioms;

(d) explain the connections between properties of a group table and the group axioms.

The advantage of defining a group $(G, \circ)$ as a general set G, together with a binary operation $\circ$ satisfying the four axioms G1–G4, is that anything we can prove directly from the axioms (in the general case) must apply to any group (any specific case). Thus, by giving one proof, we can simultaneously establish a result that holds for groups of symmetries, modular arithmetic groups, infinite groups of real or complex numbers, and many more.

In this section we introduce some important properties, and show how these can be derived from the group axioms. However, we do not expect you to be able to produce or reproduce these proofs. On your first reading, concentrate on the group properties and examples, and leave detailed study of the proofs until later. When you are familiar with the basic ideas, you should concentrate on the uniqueness proofs in Subsection 4.1, which impart the 'flavour' of proofs in group theory. In general, such proofs are short and, in some senses, simple. However, a beginner in group theory is unlikely to think of them unaided. They involve writing down *what you know*, thinking about *what you want to prove* and trying to *bridge the gap* in an inspired way by using one or more of the group axioms (there are only four from which to choose).

4.1   Uniqueness properties

Uniqueness of the identity element

Axiom G2 states that, in every group $(G, \circ)$, there must be an identity element e such that, for all $g \in G$,

$$g \circ e = g = e \circ g.$$

Each of our examples of groups has contained precisely *one* identity element, and we shall prove now that this must always be the case. We say that the identity in a group is *unique*.

Property 4.1   In any group, the identity element is unique.

As a result of this property we can, and shall, refer to *the* identity element.

The proof of this result is short and not difficult—once you know what to do. We have set out the proof below, with comments to motivate the steps.

Comments

We use a standard method for proving uniqueness:

we show that if e and e' are identity elements in G, then they must be equal.

We write down what we know:

   e is an identity element

and

   e' is an identity element.

We wish to relate e and e'.

We use particular cases of the general equations (4.1) and (4.2). We put

  $g = e'$ in equation (4.1)

and

  $g = e$ in equation (4.2).

We use equations (4.3) and (4.4) to simplify the element $e \circ e'$ in two different ways.

We now have

  $e' = e \circ e' = e,$

as required.

Proof

Suppose that e and e' are identity elements in the group $(G, \circ)$.

We want to show that $e = e'$ is the only possibility.

By axiom G2, we know that

$$g \circ e = g = e \circ g \quad \text{for all } g \in G, \qquad (4.1)$$

and

$$g \circ e' = g = e' \circ g \quad \text{for all } g \in G. \qquad (4.2)$$

Equations (4.1) and (4.2) hold for *all* $g \in G$; so, in particular,

$$e' \circ e = e' = e \circ e' \qquad (4.3)$$

and

$$e \circ e' = e = e' \circ e. \qquad (4.4)$$

From the right-hand part of equation (4.3),

$$e' = e \circ e',$$

and from the left-hand part of equation (4.4),

$$e \circ e' = e.$$

Thus

$$e = e',$$

so $(G, \circ)$ has a unique identity element. ∎

Uniqueness of the inverse element

Axiom G3 states that, for each element g in a group $(G, \circ)$, there must exist an inverse element $g^{-1} \in G$ such that

$$g \circ g^{-1} = e = g^{-1} \circ g.$$

In each group that we have met so far, the inverse of each element is unique: no element has two distinct inverses.

Property 4.2   In any group, each element has a unique inverse.

As a result of this property we can, and shall, refer to *the* inverse of a particular group element.

Again the proof is short: we apply the axiom G4 (associativity) to a particular expression.

Comments

Again, we use the standard method for proving uniqueness:

we show that if x and y are inverses of $g \in G$, then they must be equal.

We write down what we know:

  x is an inverse of g

and

  y is an inverse of g.

Proof

Suppose that $g \in G$ has inverse elements—x and y.

We want to show that $x = y$ is the only possibility.

Let e be the identity element in G.

By axiom G3, we know that

$$g \circ x = e = x \circ g \qquad (4.5)$$

and

$$g \circ y = e = y \circ g. \qquad (4.6)$$

We wish to relate x and y.

We consider the element
$$y \circ g \circ x,$$
and simplify it in two different ways.

We have
$$y \circ g \circ x = y \circ (g \circ x),$$
which simplifies to y.

Also
$$y \circ g \circ x = (y \circ g) \circ x,$$
which simplifies to x.

Now we use associativity:
$$y \circ (g \circ x) = (y \circ g) \circ x,$$
which simplifies to $y = x$.

We now have
$$y = x,$$
as required.

Consider the element
$$y \circ g \circ x.$$
From the left-hand part of equation (4.5),
$$g \circ x = e,$$
so
$$y \circ (g \circ x) = y \circ e$$
$$= y, \tag{4.7}$$
since e is the identity.

From the right-hand part of equation (4.6),
$$y \circ g = e,$$
so
$$(y \circ g) \circ x = e \circ x$$
$$= x, \tag{4.8}$$
since e is the identity.

By axiom G4,
$$y \circ (g \circ x) = (y \circ g) \circ x.$$
By equation (4.7), the left-hand side is y.
By equation (4.8), the right-hand side is x.

Thus
$$y = x,$$
so g has a unique inverse in G. ∎

4.2 Properties of inverses

Inverse of the inverse

In our work on groups we have found that some elements are self-inverse, and the remaining elements can be arranged in pairs of elements that are inverses of each other. In other words, if g^{-1} is the inverse of g, then g is the inverse of g^{-1}. We state this as Property 4.3.

Property 4.3 In any group $(G, \circ)$,

if $g \in G$ and g has inverse $g^{-1} \in G$, then g^{-1} has inverse g.

In symbols, we write
$$(g^{-1})^{-1} = g.$$

Proof Let $g \in G$ and let g^{-1} be the inverse of g. By axiom G3,
$$g \circ g^{-1} = e = g^{-1} \circ g.$$

Altering the order of the expressions, we obtain
$$g^{-1} \circ g = e = g \circ g^{-1}.$$

This tells us that g is an inverse of g^{-1}. Hence, by Property 4.2 (uniqueness of the inverse), we have
$$(g^{-1})^{-1} = g. \quad ∎$$

Inverse of a composite

Our second property of inverses concerns the inverse of a composite.

If f and g are symmetries of a plane figure F, then the inverse of $g \circ f$ is $f^{-1} \circ g^{-1}$.

This result is true of composites in general (whenever inverses exist).

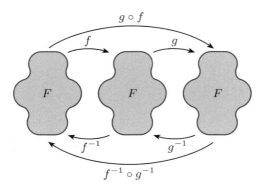

To undo 'f then g', we first undo g, then undo f; that is, we do 'g^{-1} then f^{-1}'.

This result is true for all groups.

> **Property 4.4**   In any group $(G, \circ)$, with $x, y \in G$,
>
> $$(x \circ y)^{-1} = y^{-1} \circ x^{-1}.$$

The strategy of the proof is identical to that of the proof for Property 4.3. We show that $y^{-1} \circ x^{-1}$ is an inverse of $x \circ y$ and then use Property 4.2 (uniqueness of the inverse).

Proof   Let $x, y \in G$. First, we compose $x \circ y$ with $y^{-1} \circ x^{-1}$ on the right:

$$
\begin{aligned}
(x \circ y) \circ (y^{-1} \circ x^{-1}) &= x \circ y \circ y^{-1} \circ x^{-1} \quad \text{(associativity)} \\
&= x \circ (y \circ y^{-1}) \circ x^{-1} \quad \text{(associativity)} \\
&= x \circ e \circ x^{-1} \quad \text{(inverses)} \\
&= x \circ x^{-1} \quad \text{(identity)} \\
&= e \quad \text{(inverses)}.
\end{aligned}
$$

Next we compose $x \circ y$ with $y^{-1} \circ x^{-1}$ on the left:

$$
\begin{aligned}
(y^{-1} \circ x^{-1}) \circ (x \circ y) &= y^{-1} \circ x^{-1} \circ x \circ y \quad \text{(associativity)} \\
&= y^{-1} \circ (x^{-1} \circ x) \circ y \quad \text{(associativity)} \\
&= y^{-1} \circ e \circ y \quad \text{(inverses)} \\
&= y^{-1} \circ y \quad \text{(identity)} \\
&= e \quad \text{(inverses)}.
\end{aligned}
$$

Hence $y^{-1} \circ x^{-1}$ is an inverse of $x \circ y$. So, by Property 4.2, it is *the* inverse of $x \circ y$; that is,

$$(x \circ y)^{-1} = y^{-1} \circ x^{-1}. \quad \blacksquare$$

4.3 Properties of group tables

For a small group $(G, \circ)$, we may construct a Cayley table for the binary operation $\circ$. Often, when we know that $(G, \circ)$ is a group and we wish to stress this, we refer to the Cayley table as a *group table*. A group table has a number of properties that correspond directly to the group axioms, so when checking whether a given Cayley table describes a group, we can use these properties to check some of the group axioms. In this subsection we discuss some of the properties of group tables, starting with those linked to the group axioms.

G1 CLOSURE   For all $g_1, g_2 \in G$,
$$g_1 \circ g_2 \in G.$$

This means simply that we can complete the body of the Cayley table using the elements of G: no new elements are required to complete the table; that is, no elements from outside G are required.

G2 IDENTITY   There exists an identity element $e \in G$ such that, for all $g \in G$,
$$g \circ e = g = e \circ g.$$

The composites $g \circ e$, for all $g \in G$, form the column of the Cayley table labelled by e. Similarly, the composites $e \circ g$, for all $g \in G$, form the row of the Cayley table labelled by e. Hence, if a Cayley table is a group table, then the column and the row corresponding to e must repeat the borders of the table.

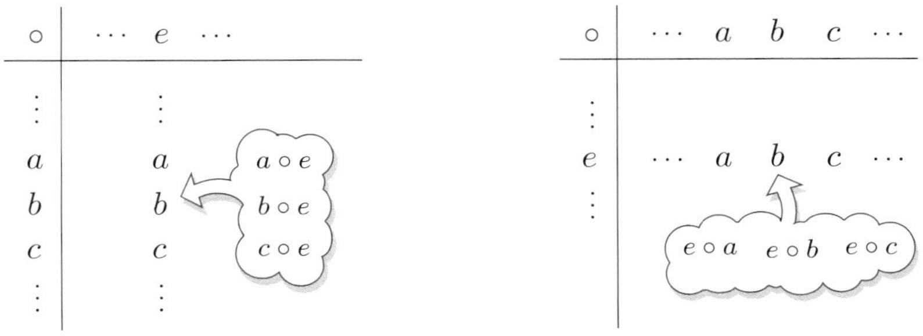

When we know which element is the identity, we normally write this label first.

Exercise 4.1   Decide which is the identity element in each of the following group tables.

(a)

$\circ$	O	E
O	E	O
E	O	E

(b)

$\circ$	D	I
D	D	I
I	I	D

(c)

$\circ$	u	v	w	x
u	w	x	u	v
v	x	w	v	u
w	u	v	w	x
x	v	u	x	w

G3 INVERSES   For each $g \in G$, there exists an inverse element $g^{-1} \in G$ such that
$$g \circ g^{-1} = e = g^{-1} \circ g.$$

The fact that each element has a unique inverse means that

the identity e must occur exactly once in each row and each column.

However, there is a slightly stronger result. If an element g is self-inverse, then $g \circ g = e$ and so e must occur on the leading diagonal. If g is not self-inverse, then g and g^{-1} are distinct elements which are inverses of each other, so the entries in the Cayley table for $g \circ g^{-1} = e$ and $g^{-1} \circ g = e$ are placed symmetrically with respect to the leading diagonal. These observations are illustrated in the following diagram.

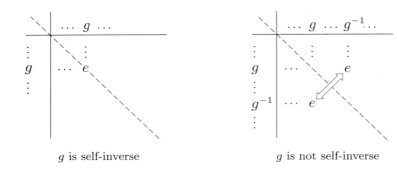

g is self-inverse g is not self-inverse

Thus a group table has the following property.

Property 4.5   In any group table, the identity e must occur exactly once in each row and each column of the table, and e must occur in symmetrical positions with respect to the leading diagonal.

Exercise 4.2   Given that the following table is a group table, draw up a table of the inverses of the eight elements.

$\circ$	a	b	c	d	e	f	g	h
a	f	e	g	h	a	b	d	c
b	e	f	h	g	b	a	c	d
c	h	g	f	e	c	d	b	a
d	g	h	e	f	d	c	a	b
e	a	b	c	d	e	f	g	h
f	b	a	d	c	f	e	h	g
g	c	d	a	b	g	h	f	e
h	d	c	b	a	h	g	e	f

Exercise 4.3   In the Cayley table below, the identity element e occurs in each row and column, but the table is not a group table. Explain why not.

$\circ$	e	a	b	c	d
e	e	a	b	c	d
a	a	b	d	e	c
b	b	e	c	d	a
c	c	d	e	a	b
d	d	c	a	b	e

G4 ASSOCIATIVITY   For all $g_1, g_2, g_3 \in G$,
$$g_1 \circ (g_2 \circ g_3) = (g_1 \circ g_2) \circ g_3.$$

It is not easy to deduce anything about associativity simply from a Cayley table. (You have to do a lot of checking.) Unfortunately, it is possible for a Cayley table to show the features corresponding to axioms G1, G2 and G3 even when the operation $\circ$ is not associative. This is illustrated by the following table.

$\circ$	e	a	b	c	d
e	e	a	b	c	d
a	a	e	c	d	b
b	b	d	e	a	c
c	c	b	d	e	a
d	d	c	a	b	e

From this table we find that:

the set is closed under $\circ$,

e is an identity element,

each element is self-inverse.

However, $\circ$ is not associative, as we saw in Frame 15.

Another property of a group table that we mentioned in Frame 15 is the following.

Property 4.6   In a group table, each element of the group occurs exactly once in each row and exactly once in each column.

We prove this statement for rows.

Proof   We prove that any given element, g say, appears exactly once in any given row—the row labelled h, say. This is equivalent to proving that there is a *unique* element of the group, x say, such that

$$h \circ x = g. \tag{4.9}$$

This equation can be 'solved' for the unknown element x by applying the inverse h^{-1} on the left:

$$h^{-1} \circ (h \circ x) = h^{-1} \circ g.$$

Hence

$$(h^{-1} \circ h) \circ x = h^{-1} \circ g \quad \text{(associativity)},$$

so

$$e \circ x = h^{-1} \circ g \quad \text{(inverses)},$$

giving

$$x = h^{-1} \circ g \quad \text{(identity)}.$$

Thus the only possible solution to equation (4.9) is $x = h^{-1} \circ g$, and this is indeed a solution, since

$$h \circ (h^{-1} \circ g) = (h \circ h^{-1}) \circ g = e \circ g = g.$$

Thus, in the row labelled h, the element g appears once, in the column labelled by the element $h^{-1} \circ g$.   ∎

The proof for columns is similar.

	$\cdots$ x $\cdots$
$\vdots$	$\vdots$
h	$\cdots$ g $\cdots$
$\vdots$	$\vdots$

By the inverse and closure axioms, $h^{-1} \circ g$ is an element of G.

The following Cancellation Laws are also proved using the inverse.

Property 4.7 Cancellation Laws

In any group $(G, \circ)$ with elements a, b and x:

if $x \circ a = x \circ b$,   then $a = b$,

if $a \circ x = b \circ x$,   then $a = b$.

Exercise 4.4   Prove the Cancellation Laws for a group $(G, \circ)$, namely:

(a) if $x \circ a = x \circ b$, then $a = b$;

(b) if $a \circ x = b \circ x$, then $a = b$.

The last property of group tables that we shall note concerns commutativity.

For any elements g_1 and g_2 of a group G, the entries corresponding to the composites $g_1 \circ g_2$ and $g_2 \circ g_1$ are symmetrically placed with respect to the leading diagonal of the group table (because the order of elements across the top and down the side is the same).

Thus, for an Abelian group, symmetrically-placed entries must be the same.

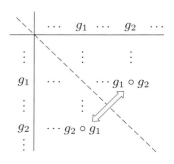

> **Property 4.8**   For an Abelian group, the group table is symmetrical about the leading diagonal.

The following group tables show that $(\mathbb{Z}_6, +_6)$ is an Abelian group, whereas $(S(\triangle), \circ)$ is not.

$(\mathbb{Z}_6, +_6)$

$+_6$	0	1	2	3	4	5
0	0	1	2	3	4	5
1	1	2	3	4	5	0
2	2	3	4	5	0	1
3	3	4	5	0	1	2
4	4	5	0	1	2	3
5	5	0	1	2	3	4

symmetrical

$(S(\triangle), \circ)$

$\circ$	e	a	b	r	s	t
e	e	a	b	r	s	t
a	a	b	e	t	r	s
b	b	e	a	s	t	r
r	r	s	t	e	a	b
s	s	t	r	b	e	a
t	t	r	s	a	b	e

not symmetrical

For example, in $S(\triangle)$,
$$a \circ r = t \quad \text{and} \quad r \circ a = s.$$

Exercise 4.5   Each of the following tables is a group table for a group of order 8 with identity e. In each case, draw up a table of inverses and state whether the group is Abelian.

(a)

	e	a	b	c	d	f	g	h
e	e	a	b	c	d	f	g	h
a	a	e	c	b	f	d	h	g
b	b	c	e	a	g	h	d	f
c	c	b	a	e	h	g	f	d
d	d	f	g	h	e	a	b	c
f	f	d	h	g	a	e	c	b
g	g	h	d	f	b	c	e	a
h	h	g	f	d	c	b	a	e

(b)

	e	a	b	c	d	f	g	h
e	e	a	b	c	d	f	g	h
a	a	b	c	e	f	g	h	d
b	b	c	e	a	g	h	d	f
c	c	e	a	b	h	d	f	g
d	d	h	g	f	b	a	e	c
f	f	d	h	g	c	b	a	e
g	g	f	d	h	e	c	b	a
h	h	g	f	d	a	e	c	b

Further exercises

Exercise 4.6   Given that the following tables are group tables, fill in the missing elements.

(a)

	e	a	b
e	e	a	b
a	a		
b	b		

(b)

	a	b	c	d
a	a	b	c	
b	b			a
c		d		
d	d		c	

Exercise 4.7   The following table is a group table.

	e	a	b	c	d	f	g	h
e	e	a	b	c	d	f	g	h
a	a	b	c	e	g	d	h	f
b	b	c	e	a	h	g	f	d
c	c	e	a	b	f	h	d	g
d	d	f	h	g	b	c	a	e
f	f	h	g	d	a	b	e	c
g	g	d	f	h	c	e	b	a
h	h	g	d	f	e	a	c	b

(a) Which element is the identity element?

(b) Write down the inverse of each of the elements $e, a, \ldots, h$.

(c) Is this group Abelian?

Exercise 4.8   Explain why each of the following Cayley tables is not a group table.

(a)

∘	e	a	b	c
e	e	a	b	c
a	a	b	d	e
b	b	d	a	b
c	c	e	b	a

(b)

∘	e	a	b	c
e	b	e	a	b
a	e	a	b	c
b	c	b	c	a
c	a	c	b	e

(c)

∘	e	a	b	c	d
e	e	a	b	c	d
a	a	b	d	e	c
b	b	e	c	d	a
c	c	d	e	a	b
d	d	c	a	b	e

(d)

∘	e	a	b	c	d	f
e	e	a	b	c	d	f
a	a	e	f	b	c	d
b	b	d	a	e	f	c
c	c	f	e	d	b	a
d	d	b	c	f	a	e
f	f	c	d	a	e	b

Exercise 4.9   Show that if $(G, \circ)$ is a group with an even number of elements, then there is an element $g \in G$ such that

$$g \circ g = e \quad \text{and} \quad g \neq e.$$

5   Symmetry in $\mathbb{R}^3$

After working through this section, you should be able to:

(a) describe the symmetries of some bounded three-dimensional figures;

(b) use two-line symbols to denote symmetries of three-dimensional figures, and to form composites and inverses of such symmetries;

(c) count the number of symmetries of certain polyhedra;

(d) understand why there are exactly five regular polyhedra.

5.1 Pre-programme work: symmetries of a figure in $\mathbb{R}^3$

We use the symbol $\mathbb{R}^3$ to denote three-dimensional space, in which a point is specified by three coordinates x, y, z.

Having considered symmetries of two-dimensional figures, we now extend our ideas to three-dimensional objects.

Some three-dimensional objects have symmetries that are essentially the same as those of a corresponding two-dimensional figure. For example, the six-sided bottle shown below has essentially the same symmetries as a regular hexagon. However, the symmetries of many three-dimensional objects cannot be thought of as essentially the same as the symmetries of any two-dimensional figure. A cube, for instance, has the symmetries of a square when looked at from each of three directions, and (as we shall see) other symmetries as well.

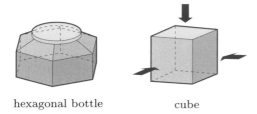

hexagonal bottle   cube

In this section we adapt the definitions of earlier sections to $\mathbb{R}^3$, and consider symmetries of three-dimensional objects.

Definition   A **figure** in $\mathbb{R}^3$ is any subset of $\mathbb{R}^3$.

This definition is very general, and includes plane figures as special cases. We shall mainly consider bounded non-planar figures with polygonal faces. Such solids are called *polyhedra*.

A *bounded* figure in $\mathbb{R}^3$ is a figure that can be surrounded by a sphere (of finite radius).

Polyhedra is the Greek for 'many faces'. The singular form is *polyhedron*.

tetrahedron   cube   hexagonal prism   truncated cube

In our examples we restrict attention to *convex polyhedra*: that is, polyhedra without dents or dimples or spikes. Of these, there are five that are of particular interest: the *regular polyhedra* (*Platonic solids*), in which all faces are congruent regular polygons and each vertex is the junction of the same numbers of edges and faces, arranged in the same way, as shown in the following diagram.

We shall show why there are only five regular polyhedra in Subsection 5.4.

| tetrahedron (4 faces) | cube (6 faces) | octahedron (8 faces) | dodecahedron (12 faces) | icosahedron (20 faces) |

Our initial definitions are almost exactly the same as those for $\mathbb{R}^2$.

Definitions   An **isometry** of $\mathbb{R}^3$ is a distance-preserving map $f : \mathbb{R}^3 \longrightarrow \mathbb{R}^3$.

A **symmetry** of a figure F in $\mathbb{R}^3$ is an isometry mapping F onto itself—that is, an isometry $f : \mathbb{R}^3 \longrightarrow \mathbb{R}^3$ such that $f(F) = F$.

Two symmetries of a figure F are **equal** if they have the same effect on F.

As for $\mathbb{R}^2$, our potential symmetries are rotations (this time about an axis of the figure in $\mathbb{R}^3$), reflections (in a plane), translations and combinations of these isometries. For a bounded figure in $\mathbb{R}^3$ (such as a polyhedron), translations alter the location of the figure and so cannot be symmetries; hence we concentrate on rotations and reflections.

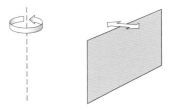

We have to be careful with rotations in $\mathbb{R}^3$, as what is clockwise when looking along an axis of rotation in one direction is anticlockwise when looking along it in the other direction. We often indicate the direction of rotation by an arrow on a diagram.

A **rotation** of F is a symmetry specified by an *axis of symmetry*, a *direction* of rotation and the *angle* through which the figure is rotated.

For example, rotation of the cube through $\pi/2$ about its vertical axis, in the direction indicated, has the following effect.

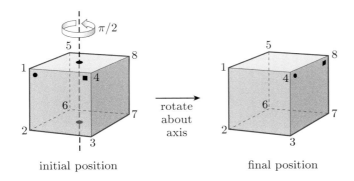

initial position   final position

Rotation arrows in $\mathbb{R}^3$ indicate the direction of rotation; they do not indicate the size of the angle through which the figure is rotated.

We shall adopt and extend our two-line symbols to record symmetries of three-dimensional objects. With the labelling shown above, this rotation is represented by

$$\begin{pmatrix} 1 & 2 & 3 & 4 & 5 & 6 & 7 & 8 \\ 4 & 3 & 7 & 8 & 1 & 2 & 6 & 5 \end{pmatrix}.$$

The identity symmetry

$$e = \begin{pmatrix} 1 & 2 & 3 & 4 & 5 & 6 & 7 & 8 \\ 1 & 2 & 3 & 4 & 5 & 6 & 7 & 8 \end{pmatrix}$$

can be thought of as a zero rotation.

A **reflection** of F is a symmetry specified by the *plane* in which the reflection takes place.

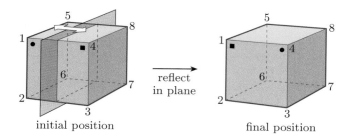

initial position   final position

The two-line symbol for the reflection shown above is

$$\begin{pmatrix} 1 & 2 & 3 & 4 & 5 & 6 & 7 & 8 \\ 4 & 3 & 2 & 1 & 8 & 7 & 6 & 5 \end{pmatrix}.$$

Composition of symmetries written as two-line symbols is similar to that for plane figures. For example, the rotation above followed by the reflection above is

$$\begin{pmatrix} 1 & 2 & 3 & 4 & 5 & 6 & 7 & 8 \\ 4 & 3 & 2 & 1 & 8 & 7 & 6 & 5 \end{pmatrix} \circ \begin{pmatrix} 1 & 2 & 3 & 4 & 5 & 6 & 7 & 8 \\ 4 & 3 & 7 & 8 & 1 & 2 & 6 & 5 \end{pmatrix}$$

$$= \begin{pmatrix} 1 & 2 & 3 & 4 & 5 & 6 & 7 & 8 \\ 1 & 2 & 6 & 5 & 4 & 3 & 7 & 8 \end{pmatrix}.$$

Remember to work from right to left.

This is a reflection in the diagonal plane passing through the locations labelled 1, 2, 7 and 8, as shown below.

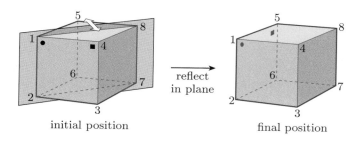

initial position   final position

To find the inverse of a symmetry given as a two-line symbol, we turn the symbol upside down. For the rotation above, we have

$$\begin{pmatrix} 1 & 2 & 3 & 4 & 5 & 6 & 7 & 8 \\ 4 & 3 & 7 & 8 & 1 & 2 & 6 & 5 \end{pmatrix}^{-1} = \begin{pmatrix} 4 & 3 & 7 & 8 & 1 & 2 & 6 & 5 \\ 1 & 2 & 3 & 4 & 5 & 6 & 7 & 8 \end{pmatrix}$$

$$= \begin{pmatrix} 1 & 2 & 3 & 4 & 5 & 6 & 7 & 8 \\ 5 & 6 & 2 & 1 & 8 & 7 & 3 & 4 \end{pmatrix}.$$

It is not necessary to reorder the columns into the natural order, but it may help with identifying the symmetry.

This is rotation of the cube through $3\pi/2$ about its vertical axis, in the direction indicated.

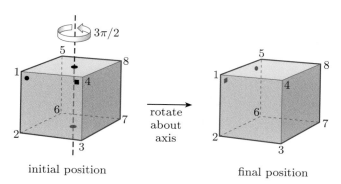

initial position   final position

Symmetries that we can demonstrate physically with a model (for polyhedra, this means rotations) are called **direct** symmetries, whereas those that we cannot show physically with the model are called **indirect** symmetries. As for plane figures, composition of direct and indirect symmetries follows a standard pattern.

We can make a second model to represent the reflected polyhedron. The images of the polyhedron under an indirect symmetry can then be illustrated by rotating this second model.

direct   ∘ direct   = direct
direct   ∘ indirect = indirect
indirect ∘ direct   = indirect
indirect ∘ indirect = direct

∘	direct	indirect
direct	direct	indirect
indirect	indirect	direct

We use $S(F)$ to denote the set of symmetries of a figure F, and $S^+(F)$ to denote the set of direct symmetries of F. The following results apply to figures in $\mathbb{R}^3$, and also to figures in $\mathbb{R}^2$.

Property 5.1

1. The set $S(F)$ of all symmetries of a figure F forms a group under composition.

2. The set $S^+(F)$ of all direct symmetries of a figure F forms a group under composition.

3. If the group $S(F)$ contains both direct and indirect symmetries and there are exactly n direct symmetries, then there are exactly n indirect symmetries. The n indirect symmetries may be obtained by composing each of the n direct symmetries with any one fixed indirect symmetry.

Watch the video programme 'Symmetry counts'.

Video

5.2 Review of the video programme

We begin by looking at various symmetrical objects which we meet in familiar situations.

Turning to mathematical objects, we pose the question: 'How can we count the number of symmetries of each of the regular polyhedra—the tetrahedron, cube, octahedron, dodecahedron and icosahedron?'

Much of the programme is devoted to answering this question for the tetrahedron.

Symmetries of the equilateral triangle

As a first step towards answering the above question, we review our approach to describing and counting symmetries of figures in $\mathbb{R}^2$; in particular, we study the symmetries of the equilateral triangle. This figure has both direct and indirect symmetries.

The direct symmetries are the identity and the two non-trivial rotations, and these form a group. Since there are three direct symmetries, there must be three indirect symmetries. We can find the three indirect symmetries by composing each of the direct symmetries with any one of the indirect symmetries. (See the following diagram.)

See the solution to Exercise 1.9(a).

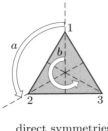
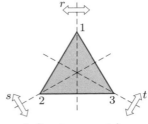

direct symmetries
e, a, b

indirect symmetries
$r = a \circ s, \; s = e \circ s, \; t = b \circ s$

Thus we obtain the following group table.

$\circ$	e	a	b	r	s	t
e	e	a	b	r	s	t
a	a	b	e	t	r	s
b	b	e	a	s	t	r
r	r	s	t	e	a	b
s	s	t	r	b	e	a
t	t	r	s	a	b	e

$\circ$	direct	indirect
direct	direct	indirect
indirect	indirect	direct

The table for the group of direct symmetries appears as a 'subtable'.

This is another example of 'blocking' in a group table.

We can represent these symmetries as the two-line symbols:

$$e = \begin{pmatrix} 1 & 2 & 3 \\ 1 & 2 & 3 \end{pmatrix}, \quad a = \begin{pmatrix} 1 & 2 & 3 \\ 2 & 3 & 1 \end{pmatrix}, \quad b = \begin{pmatrix} 1 & 2 & 3 \\ 3 & 1 & 2 \end{pmatrix},$$

$$r = \begin{pmatrix} 1 & 2 & 3 \\ 1 & 3 & 2 \end{pmatrix}, \quad s = \begin{pmatrix} 1 & 2 & 3 \\ 3 & 2 & 1 \end{pmatrix}, \quad t = \begin{pmatrix} 1 & 2 & 3 \\ 2 & 1 & 3 \end{pmatrix}.$$

See the solution to Exercise 2.3.

Symmetries of the regular tetrahedron

Next we consider the symmetries of the regular tetrahedron. The identity symmetry e leaves the tetrahedron as it is and is a direct symmetry. Also, for each of the four vertices, there are two non-trivial direct symmetries—namely rotations through angles $2\pi/3$ and $4\pi/3$ about an axis through the vertex from the centre of the opposite face. Thus these correspond to anticlockwise rotations of the triangular face opposite the fixed vertex, when viewed from outside the tetrahedron, looking directly at the face.

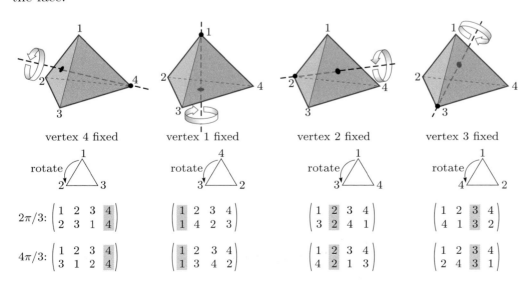

vertex 4 fixed

vertex 1 fixed

vertex 2 fixed

vertex 3 fixed

$2\pi/3$: $\begin{pmatrix} 1 & 2 & 3 & 4 \\ 2 & 3 & 1 & 4 \end{pmatrix}$ $\quad \begin{pmatrix} 1 & 2 & 3 & 4 \\ 1 & 4 & 2 & 3 \end{pmatrix}$ $\quad \begin{pmatrix} 1 & 2 & 3 & 4 \\ 3 & 2 & 4 & 1 \end{pmatrix}$ $\quad \begin{pmatrix} 1 & 2 & 3 & 4 \\ 4 & 1 & 3 & 2 \end{pmatrix}$

$4\pi/3$: $\begin{pmatrix} 1 & 2 & 3 & 4 \\ 3 & 1 & 2 & 4 \end{pmatrix}$ $\quad \begin{pmatrix} 1 & 2 & 3 & 4 \\ 1 & 3 & 4 & 2 \end{pmatrix}$ $\quad \begin{pmatrix} 1 & 2 & 3 & 4 \\ 4 & 2 & 1 & 3 \end{pmatrix}$ $\quad \begin{pmatrix} 1 & 2 & 3 & 4 \\ 2 & 4 & 3 & 1 \end{pmatrix}$

Now we have nine direct symmetries, but are there any more? We know that the set of direct symmetries of the tetrahedron is a group, so it must be closed under composition. So we test for closure by composing some of the symmetries given above.

The symmetry obtained by performing first the rotation through $2\pi/3$ which fixes the vertex at location 1, and then the rotation through $4\pi/3$ which fixes the vertex at location 2, is

$$\begin{pmatrix} 1 & 2 & 3 & 4 \\ 4 & 2 & 1 & 3 \end{pmatrix} \circ \begin{pmatrix} 1 & 2 & 3 & 4 \\ 1 & 4 & 2 & 3 \end{pmatrix} = \begin{pmatrix} 1 & 2 & 3 & 4 \\ 4 & 3 & 2 & 1 \end{pmatrix},$$

which is not one of the symmetries already listed. It is a new direct symmetry, which simultaneously interchanges the vertices at locations 1 and 4 and the vertices at locations 2 and 3. Geometrically, it corresponds to a rotation through π about an axis through the midpoints of the opposite edges joining 1 to 4 and 2 to 3.

A similar rotation of the tetrahedron exists for each of the other two pairs of opposite edges. Thus we have found three further direct symmetries.

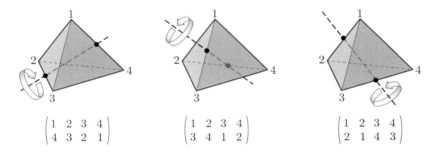

$$\begin{pmatrix} 1 & 2 & 3 & 4 \\ 4 & 3 & 2 & 1 \end{pmatrix} \qquad \begin{pmatrix} 1 & 2 & 3 & 4 \\ 3 & 4 & 1 & 2 \end{pmatrix} \qquad \begin{pmatrix} 1 & 2 & 3 & 4 \\ 2 & 1 & 4 & 3 \end{pmatrix}$$

We have now found the following 12 direct symmetries of the tetrahedron.

$$\begin{pmatrix} 1 & 2 & 3 & 4 \\ 1 & 2 & 3 & 4 \end{pmatrix} \quad \begin{pmatrix} 1 & 2 & 3 & 4 \\ 2 & 3 & 1 & 4 \end{pmatrix} \quad \begin{pmatrix} 1 & 2 & 3 & 4 \\ 3 & 1 & 2 & 4 \end{pmatrix} \quad \begin{pmatrix} 1 & 2 & 3 & 4 \\ 4 & 3 & 2 & 1 \end{pmatrix}$$

$$\begin{pmatrix} 1 & 2 & 3 & 4 \\ 1 & 4 & 2 & 3 \end{pmatrix} \quad \begin{pmatrix} 1 & 2 & 3 & 4 \\ 3 & 2 & 4 & 1 \end{pmatrix} \quad \begin{pmatrix} 1 & 2 & 3 & 4 \\ 4 & 1 & 3 & 2 \end{pmatrix} \quad \begin{pmatrix} 1 & 2 & 3 & 4 \\ 3 & 4 & 1 & 2 \end{pmatrix}$$

$$\begin{pmatrix} 1 & 2 & 3 & 4 \\ 1 & 3 & 4 & 2 \end{pmatrix} \quad \begin{pmatrix} 1 & 2 & 3 & 4 \\ 4 & 2 & 1 & 3 \end{pmatrix} \quad \begin{pmatrix} 1 & 2 & 3 & 4 \\ 2 & 4 & 3 & 1 \end{pmatrix} \quad \begin{pmatrix} 1 & 2 & 3 & 4 \\ 2 & 1 & 4 & 3 \end{pmatrix}$$

We can see that there are only 12 direct symmetries as follows. Imagine picking up the tetrahedron shown below, and placing it down again to occupy the same space it occupied originally, but possibly with the vertices at new locations. We count the number of ways of doing this. We can choose any of the 4 faces as the 'base' of the tetrahedron, and then there are 3 ways of placing the tetrahedron on this base, corresponding to the 3 rotational symmetries of the base triangle. Thus altogether there are $4 \times 3 = 12$ ways of placing the tetrahedron—that is, 12 direct symmetries.

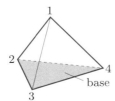

There are also indirect symmetries of the tetrahedron—for example, a reflection in the vertical plane through the edge joining the vertices at locations 1 and 3 and the midpoint of the edge joining the vertices at locations 2 and 4.

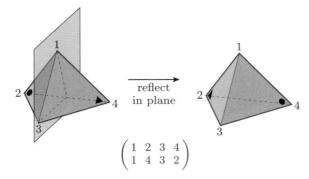

$$\begin{pmatrix} 1 & 2 & 3 & 4 \\ 1 & 4 & 3 & 2 \end{pmatrix}$$

It follows that the tetrahedron has 12 indirect symmetries, which can be obtained by composing each of the 12 direct symmetries with the above indirect symmetry on the right.

We perform first the indirect symmetry and then the direct symmetry. This is equivalent to applying the twelve direct symmetries to the 'reflected' tetrahedron.

$$\begin{pmatrix} 1 & 2 & 3 & 4 \\ 1 & 4 & 3 & 2 \end{pmatrix} \quad \begin{pmatrix} 1 & 2 & 3 & 4 \\ 2 & 4 & 1 & 3 \end{pmatrix} \quad \begin{pmatrix} 1 & 2 & 3 & 4 \\ 3 & 4 & 2 & 1 \end{pmatrix} \quad \begin{pmatrix} 1 & 2 & 3 & 4 \\ 4 & 1 & 2 & 3 \end{pmatrix}$$

$$\begin{pmatrix} 1 & 2 & 3 & 4 \\ 1 & 3 & 2 & 4 \end{pmatrix} \quad \begin{pmatrix} 1 & 2 & 3 & 4 \\ 3 & 1 & 4 & 2 \end{pmatrix} \quad \begin{pmatrix} 1 & 2 & 3 & 4 \\ 4 & 2 & 3 & 1 \end{pmatrix} \quad \begin{pmatrix} 1 & 2 & 3 & 4 \\ 3 & 2 & 1 & 4 \end{pmatrix}$$

$$\begin{pmatrix} 1 & 2 & 3 & 4 \\ 1 & 2 & 4 & 3 \end{pmatrix} \quad \begin{pmatrix} 1 & 2 & 3 & 4 \\ 4 & 3 & 1 & 2 \end{pmatrix} \quad \begin{pmatrix} 1 & 2 & 3 & 4 \\ 2 & 1 & 3 & 4 \end{pmatrix} \quad \begin{pmatrix} 1 & 2 & 3 & 4 \\ 2 & 3 & 4 & 1 \end{pmatrix}$$

Thus the tetrahedron has 24 symmetries.

Another way of obtaining the number 24 is as follows. We count the number of ways of replacing the tetrahedron, or the reflected tetrahedron, in the space occupied originally by the tetrahedron, but possibly with the vertices at new locations. We can choose any of the 4 faces to be placed as the base. Each of the 6 symmetries of such a face gives a symmetry of the tetrahedron, so there are 6 ways of replacing the tetrahedron, or the reflected tetrahedron, on this base. Thus there are $4 \times 6 = 24$ symmetries of the tetrahedron.

Symmetries of the regular polyhedra

For any regular polyhedron, each symmetry of a face gives a symmetry of the polyhedron. Therefore an argument similar to that for the tetrahedron shows that the total number of symmetries of a regular polyhedron is the number of faces multiplied by the number of symmetries of each face. Thus we have the following strategy.

Strategy 5.1   To determine the number of symmetries of a regular polyhedron.

1. Count the number of faces.

2. Count the number of symmetries of a face.

Then,

$$\begin{pmatrix} \text{number of} \\ \text{symmetries of} \\ \text{regular polyhedron} \end{pmatrix} = \begin{pmatrix} \text{number of} \\ \text{faces} \end{pmatrix} \times \begin{pmatrix} \text{number of} \\ \text{symmetries of face} \end{pmatrix}.$$

It does not matter whether we do step 1 or step 2 first. In the video, step 2 is done first.

Post-video exercise

Exercise 5.1   Using Strategy 5.1, show that the cube and the octahedron have 48 symmetries each, and that the dodecahedron and the icosahedron have 120 symmetries each.

5.3 Symmetries of non-regular polyhedra

Strategy 5.1 for finding the number of symmetries of a regular polyhedron—multiply the number of faces by the number of symmetries of a face—can be adapted to find the number of symmetries of a non-regular polyhedron. We illustrate the method by two examples.

Pentagonal prism

We consider the pentagonal prism, in which the top and bottom faces are regular pentagons and the vertical faces are squares.

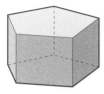

pentagonal prism   faces

This prism has direct symmetries—for example, we can rotate the prism about a vertical axis. It also has indirect symmetries—for example, we can reflect the prism in the plane that contains a vertical edge and bisects the square face opposite this edge.

To find the number of symmetries of the prism, we can count the number of ways of replacing the prism, or the reflected prism, in the space it occupied originally, but possibly with the vertices at new locations.

In the above figure, the prism is shown with a pentagonal face as its base, so we can choose either of the 2 pentagonal faces to be the base. Each of the 10 symmetries of such a face gives a symmetry of the prism, so there are 10 ways of replacing the prism, or the reflected prism, on this base. Thus there are $2 \times 10 = 20$ symmetries of the prism.

We carried out this calculation by considering one of the pentagonal faces as the base. We can check our answer by considering one of the square faces to be the base, as shown below.

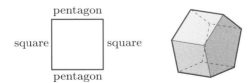

Again we count the number of ways of replacing the prism, or the reflected prism, in the space it originally occupied. We can choose any of the 5 square faces to be the base.

We now have to be careful because only some of the 8 symmetries of the square give symmetries of the prism. For example, one symmetry of the square base is a rotation of $\pi/2$ about its centre, but if we apply the corresponding transformation to the prism as a whole—that is, if we rotate the prism through $\pi/2$ about the vertical axis through the centre of the square base—then the prism does not occupy its original space in $\mathbb{R}^3$, so this is not a symmetry of the prism. Similarly, reflections through the diagonals of the square base do not give symmetries of the prism.

In fact, only 4 of the symmetries of the square base are also symmetries of the prism, namely the identity, rotation through π and reflections in the lines joining midpoints of opposite edges. Thus the number of symmetries of the prism is $5 \times 4 = 20$. This confirms our earlier answer.

Small rhombicuboctahedron

As a second example, we consider the polyhedron shown below. It is called a small rhombicuboctahedron, and it has 18 square faces and 8 faces that are equilateral triangles.

It is not to be confused with the great rhombicuboctahedron, which has 12 square faces, 8 hexagonal faces and 6 octagonal faces.

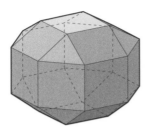

small rhombicuboctahedron

To find the number of symmetries of the polyhedron, we can count the number of ways of replacing the polyhedron, or the reflected polyhedron, in the space it occupied originally, as shown above with a square face as its base, but possibly with the vertices at new locations.

We immediately come across a new complication—only some of the square faces of the polyhedron can be placed as the base if the polyhedron, or its reflection, is to occupy its original space in $\mathbb{R}^3$. This is because there are two types of square face: in one type, all four edges of the face are joined to other square faces, whereas in the other type, two edges are joined to square faces and two to triangular faces, as shown below.

The small rhombicuboctahedron shown above has a square face of the first type as its base. There are 6 faces of this type in the polyhedron, and we can choose any of these to be placed as the base.

Next we have to determine how many of the eight symmetries of one of these square faces give symmetries of the polyhedron. Consideration of the polyhedron shows that all 8 symmetries do, so the number of symmetries of the polyhedron is $6 \times 8 = 48$.

The strategy for finding the number of symmetries of a non-regular polyhedron is now given.

Strategy 5.2   To determine the number of symmetries of a non-regular polyhedron.

1. Select one type of face and count the number of similar faces which are similarly placed in the polyhedron.

2. Count the symmetries of the face within the polyhedron (that is, symmetries of the face that are also symmetries of the polyhedron).

Then,

$$\left(\begin{array}{c} \text{number of} \\ \text{symmetries of} \\ \text{the polyhedron} \end{array} \right) = \left(\begin{array}{c} \text{number of} \\ \text{faces of the} \\ \text{selected type} \end{array} \right) \times \left(\begin{array}{c} \text{number of} \\ \text{symmetries of face} \\ \text{that are also} \\ \text{symmetries of} \\ \text{the polyhedron} \end{array} \right).$$

Exercise 5.2   Using Strategy 5.2, calculate the number of symmetries of the following figure. Check your calculations by considering the solid in a different way.

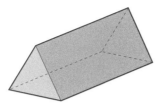

triangular prism

5.4 Platonic solids

The Platonic solids are the convex regular polyhedra in which each face is the same regular polygon and each vertex is the junction of the same number of edges and faces arranged in the same way. In order to produce a solid, we must have at least three edges (and so at least three faces) meeting at each vertex.

Starting with an equilateral triangle face, we can have three, four or five triangular faces around each vertex, but six equilateral triangles would lie flat, and more than six equilateral triangles would give a non-convex solid.

3 faces   4 faces   5 faces

The arrangement of faces at each vertex of the solid must be the same, so we can build up the rest of the solid from the construction at one vertex. The three possibilities above give the tetrahedron, the octahedron and the icosahedron, respectively.

tetrahedron   octahedron   icosahedron

Next we consider a square as a possible face. Three squares at each vertex give a cube, but four squares would lie flat, and more than four squares would give a non-convex solid.

cube   dodecahedron

The fifth Platonic solid, the dodecahedron, is formed by using three regular pentagons at each vertex. Four or more regular pentagons around a vertex would give a non-convex solid.

There can be no more such solids because three regular hexagons lie flat, and for any regular polygon with more than six edges, the angle at each vertex is greater than $2\pi/3$, so we cannot fit three together at a vertex without making the solid non-convex.

Thus there are precisely five regular polyhedra.

The Platonic solids are so named not because Plato (427–347 BC) discovered them, but because he associated the regular tetrahedron, cube, octahedron and icosahedron with the four elements of fire, earth, air and water, respectively; he associated the dodecahedron with the universe.

The angle at a vertex of a regular n-gon is $\pi(n-2)/n$, which is greater than $2\pi/3$ for $n > 6$.

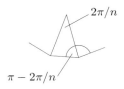

Further exercises

Exercise 5.3   Use Strategy 5.2 to count the number of symmetries of the small rhombicuboctahedron by considering:

(a) a square face, of the second type;

(b) a triangular face.

Exercise 5.4

(a) Use Strategy 5.2 to show that a rectangular block has eight symmetries.

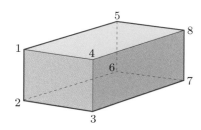

(b) Write down the two-line symbol for each of the eight symmetries, using the labelling shown above.

Solutions to the exercises

1.1 (a) We denote the initial position by a dot at the top.

The symmetries are as follows.

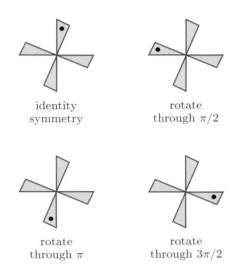

identity
symmetry

rotate
through $\pi/2$

rotate
through π

rotate
through $3\pi/2$

(b) We denote the initial position by a dot in the top left corner.

The symmetries are as follows.

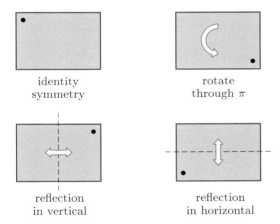

identity
symmetry

rotate
through π

reflection
in vertical

reflection
in horizontal

(c) We denote the initial position by symbols near two of the vertices.

The symmetries are as follows.

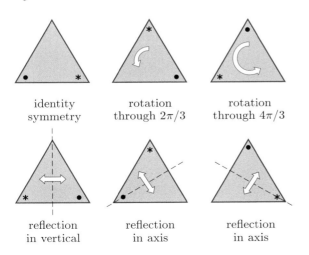

identity
symmetry

rotation
through $2\pi/3$

rotation
through $4\pi/3$

reflection
in vertical

reflection
in axis

reflection
in axis

1.2 We find the required composites by drawing diagrams similar to those in the text.

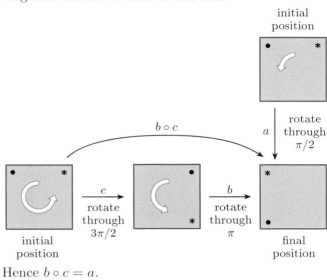

Hence $b \circ c = a$.

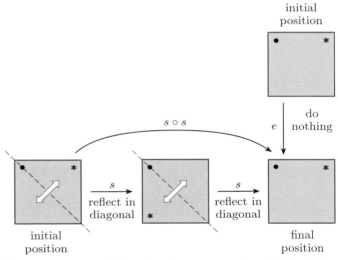

Hence $s \circ s = e$. (A reflection composed with itself is the same as the identity e.)

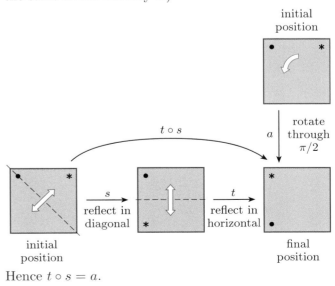

Hence $t \circ s = a$.

59

1.3 (a) The required composites are as follows.

Hence $a \circ a = b$.

Hence $a \circ b = c$.

Hence $a \circ c = e$.

The required composites are as follows.

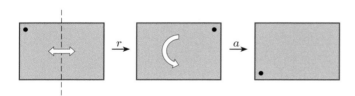

Hence $a \circ r = s$.

Hence $a \circ s = r$.

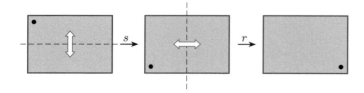

Hence $r \circ s = a$.

1.4 The required composites are as follows.

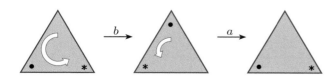

Hence $a \circ b = e$.

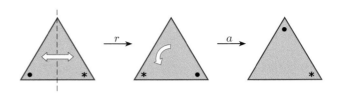

Hence $a \circ r = t$.

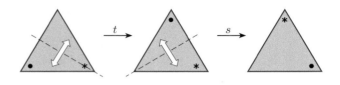

Hence $s \circ t = a$.

1.5 (a) In $S(\text{WIND})$, as in $S(\square)$, the rotations a and c are inverses of each other, and b is self-inverse.

Element	e	a	b	c
Inverse	e	c	b	a

(b) In $S(\square)$, each element is self-inverse.

Element	e	a	r	s
Inverse	e	a	r	s

(c) In $S(\triangle)$, the rotations a and b are inverses of each other, and the other symmetries are self-inverse.

Element	e	a	b	r	s	t
Inverse	e	b	a	r	s	t

1.6 In this exercise we find the composites using the diagrammatic method described in the text. (We do not give the diagrams here.)

First we find $a \circ (t \circ a)$:
$$t \circ a = s \quad \text{and} \quad a \circ s = t,$$
so $a \circ (t \circ a) = t$.

Next we find $(a \circ t) \circ a$:
$$a \circ t = u \quad \text{and} \quad u \circ a = t,$$
so $(a \circ t) \circ a = t$.

Hence
$$a \circ t \circ a = a \circ (t \circ a) = (a \circ t) \circ a.$$

1.7 We find $r_{\pi/4} \circ q_{\pi/2}$ using the following diagram.

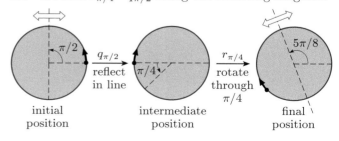

Hence $r_{\pi/4} \circ q_{\pi/2} = q_{5\pi/8}$.

1.8 Using the formulas, we obtain:

$$r_{\pi/4} \circ r_{\pi/2} = r_{(\pi/4+\pi/2) \pmod{2\pi}} = r_{3\pi/4},$$

$$q_{\pi/4} \circ q_{\pi/2} = r_{2(\pi/4-\pi/2) \pmod{2\pi}}$$
$$= r_{-\pi/2 \pmod{2\pi}} = r_{3\pi/2},$$

$$q_{\pi/4} \circ r_{\pi/2} = q_{(\pi/4 - \frac{1}{2}(\pi/2)) \pmod{\pi}} = q_0,$$

$$r_{\pi/4} \circ q_{\pi/2} = q_{(\frac{1}{2}(\pi/4) + \pi/2) \pmod{\pi}} = q_{5\pi/8}.$$

1.9 This solution uses the standard labelling for symmetries introduced in Exercises 1.3 and 1.4.

(a) $S^+(\triangle) = \{e, a, b\}$.

Using the reflection r, we obtain the following diagram.

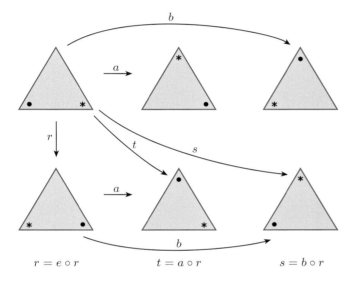

$$r = e \circ r \qquad t = a \circ r \qquad s = b \circ r$$

Instead of r, we could have used s or t as the reflection:

$$s = e \circ s, \quad r = a \circ s, \quad t = b \circ s,$$
$$t = e \circ t, \quad s = a \circ t, \quad r = b \circ t.$$

(b) $S^+(\square) = \{e, a\}$.

Using the reflection r, we obtain the following diagram.

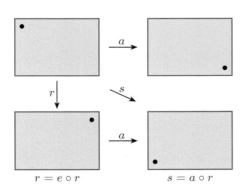

$$r = e \circ r \qquad s = a \circ r$$

Alternatively, we could have used the reflection s:

$$s = e \circ s, \quad r = a \circ s.$$

1.10 (a) Parallelogram

The symmetries are:

the identity;

rotation about the centre through π.

(b) Rhombus

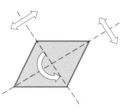

The symmetries are:

the identity;

rotation about the centre through π;

reflection in each diagonal.

(c) Symmetrical trapezium

The symmetries are:

the identity;

reflection in the line bisecting the two parallel edges.

(d) Regular star

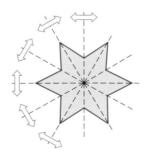

The symmetries are:

six anticlockwise rotations about the centre through 0, $\pi/3$, $2\pi/3$, π, $4\pi/3$ and $5\pi/3$;

six reflections, three in lines joining opposite vertices and three in lines joining opposite reflex angles.

(Only the reflections are shown on the figure.)

(e) Circular sawblade

The symmetries are:

six anticlockwise rotations about the centre through 0, $\pi/3$, $2\pi/3$, π, $4\pi/3$ and $5\pi/3$.

(Two of these rotations, through $2\pi/3$ and $5\pi/3$, are illustrated on the figure. The figure has no reflectional symmetry.)

1.11 The required composites are as follows.

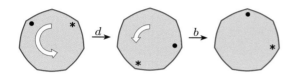

Hence $b \circ d = g$.

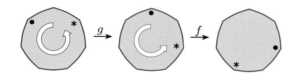

Hence $f \circ g = d$.

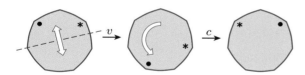

Hence $c \circ v = r$.

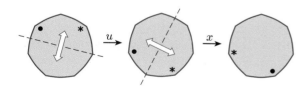

Hence $x \circ u = c$.

1.12

	Rotations	Reflections
Element	e a b c d f g	r s t u v w x
Inverse	e g f d c b a	r s t u v w x

Note that each of the reflections is its own inverse.

1.13 The direct symmetries are the seven rotations e, a, b, c, d, f, g.

The indirect symmetries x, r and s are obtained by composing w with the rotations a, b and c, respectively:

$$x = a \circ w, \quad r = b \circ w, \quad s = c \circ w.$$

We can picture this as follows.

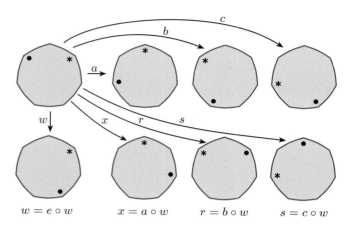

Similarly, the indirect symmetries t, u and v are obtained by composing w with the rotations d, f and g, respectively:

$$t = d \circ w, \quad u = f \circ w, \quad v = g \circ w.$$

We can picture this as follows.

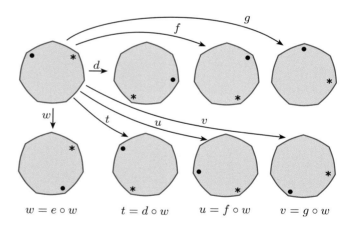

2.1 We have

$$b = \begin{pmatrix} 1 & 2 & 3 & 4 \\ 3 & 4 & 1 & 2 \end{pmatrix}, \quad c = \begin{pmatrix} 1 & 2 & 3 & 4 \\ 4 & 1 & 2 & 3 \end{pmatrix},$$

$$s = \begin{pmatrix} 1 & 2 & 3 & 4 \\ 1 & 4 & 3 & 2 \end{pmatrix}, \quad u = \begin{pmatrix} 1 & 2 & 3 & 4 \\ 3 & 2 & 1 & 4 \end{pmatrix}.$$

2.2 Here
$$e = \begin{pmatrix} 1 & 2 & 3 & 4 \\ 1 & 2 & 3 & 4 \end{pmatrix}, \quad a = \begin{pmatrix} 1 & 2 & 3 & 4 \\ 4 & 3 & 2 & 1 \end{pmatrix},$$
$$r = \begin{pmatrix} 1 & 2 & 3 & 4 \\ 2 & 1 & 4 & 3 \end{pmatrix}, \quad s = \begin{pmatrix} 1 & 2 & 3 & 4 \\ 3 & 4 & 1 & 2 \end{pmatrix}.$$

2.3 We have
$$e = \begin{pmatrix} 1 & 2 & 3 \\ 1 & 2 & 3 \end{pmatrix}, \quad a = \begin{pmatrix} 1 & 2 & 3 \\ 2 & 3 & 1 \end{pmatrix}, \quad b = \begin{pmatrix} 1 & 2 & 3 \\ 3 & 1 & 2 \end{pmatrix},$$
$$r = \begin{pmatrix} 1 & 2 & 3 \\ 1 & 3 & 2 \end{pmatrix}, \quad s = \begin{pmatrix} 1 & 2 & 3 \\ 3 & 2 & 1 \end{pmatrix}, \quad t = \begin{pmatrix} 1 & 2 & 3 \\ 2 & 1 & 3 \end{pmatrix}.$$

2.4

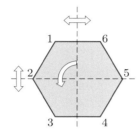

(a) $\begin{pmatrix} 1 & 2 & 3 & 4 & 5 & 6 \\ 6 & 5 & 4 & 3 & 2 & 1 \end{pmatrix}$ represents reflection in the vertical axis of symmetry joining the midpoints of the edges $1, 6$ and $3, 4$.

(b) $\begin{pmatrix} 1 & 2 & 3 & 4 & 5 & 6 \\ 3 & 4 & 5 & 6 & 1 & 2 \end{pmatrix}$ represents anticlockwise rotation through $2\pi/3$ about the centre.

(c) $\begin{pmatrix} 1 & 2 & 3 & 4 & 5 & 6 \\ 3 & 2 & 1 & 6 & 5 & 4 \end{pmatrix}$ represents reflection in the horizontal axis of symmetry through locations 2 and 5.

2.5 We have
$$a \circ a = \begin{pmatrix} 1 & 2 & 3 \\ 2 & 3 & 1 \end{pmatrix} \circ \begin{pmatrix} 1 & 2 & 3 \\ 2 & 3 & 1 \end{pmatrix} = \begin{pmatrix} 1 & 2 & 3 \\ 3 & 1 & 2 \end{pmatrix} = b,$$
$$b \circ s = \begin{pmatrix} 1 & 2 & 3 \\ 3 & 1 & 2 \end{pmatrix} \circ \begin{pmatrix} 1 & 2 & 3 \\ 3 & 2 & 1 \end{pmatrix} = \begin{pmatrix} 1 & 2 & 3 \\ 2 & 1 & 3 \end{pmatrix} = t,$$
$$s \circ b = \begin{pmatrix} 1 & 2 & 3 \\ 3 & 2 & 1 \end{pmatrix} \circ \begin{pmatrix} 1 & 2 & 3 \\ 3 & 1 & 2 \end{pmatrix} = \begin{pmatrix} 1 & 2 & 3 \\ 1 & 3 & 2 \end{pmatrix} = r,$$
$$t \circ s = \begin{pmatrix} 1 & 2 & 3 \\ 2 & 1 & 3 \end{pmatrix} \circ \begin{pmatrix} 1 & 2 & 3 \\ 3 & 2 & 1 \end{pmatrix} = \begin{pmatrix} 1 & 2 & 3 \\ 3 & 1 & 2 \end{pmatrix} = b.$$

2.6 In each case we turn the symbol upside down and reorder the columns.

(a) $\begin{pmatrix} 1 & 2 & 3 & 4 & 5 & 6 \\ 5 & 6 & 1 & 2 & 3 & 4 \end{pmatrix}^{-1} = \begin{pmatrix} 5 & 6 & 1 & 2 & 3 & 4 \\ 1 & 2 & 3 & 4 & 5 & 6 \end{pmatrix}$
$$= \begin{pmatrix} 1 & 2 & 3 & 4 & 5 & 6 \\ 3 & 4 & 5 & 6 & 1 & 2 \end{pmatrix}$$

(b) $\begin{pmatrix} 1 & 2 & 3 & 4 & 5 & 6 \\ 2 & 1 & 6 & 5 & 4 & 3 \end{pmatrix}^{-1} = \begin{pmatrix} 2 & 1 & 6 & 5 & 4 & 3 \\ 1 & 2 & 3 & 4 & 5 & 6 \end{pmatrix}$
$$= \begin{pmatrix} 1 & 2 & 3 & 4 & 5 & 6 \\ 2 & 1 & 6 & 5 & 4 & 3 \end{pmatrix}$$

(c) $\begin{pmatrix} 1 & 2 & 3 & 4 & 5 & 6 \\ 4 & 5 & 6 & 1 & 2 & 3 \end{pmatrix}^{-1} = \begin{pmatrix} 4 & 5 & 6 & 1 & 2 & 3 \\ 1 & 2 & 3 & 4 & 5 & 6 \end{pmatrix}$
$$= \begin{pmatrix} 1 & 2 & 3 & 4 & 5 & 6 \\ 4 & 5 & 6 & 1 & 2 & 3 \end{pmatrix}$$

2.7 The Cayley table for $S(\triangle)$ is as follows.

$\circ$	e	a	b	r	s	t
e	e	a	b	r	s	t
a	a	b	e	t	r	s
b	b	e	a	s	t	r
r	r	s	t	e	a	b
s	s	t	r	b	e	a
t	t	r	s	a	b	e

2.8 The Cayley table for $S(\square)$ is as follows.

$\circ$	e	a	r	s
e	e	a	r	s
a	a	e	s	r
r	r	s	e	a
s	s	r	a	e

2.9

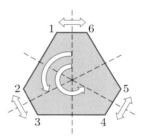

The symmetries are:

the identity,
$$\begin{pmatrix} 1 & 2 & 3 & 4 & 5 & 6 \\ 1 & 2 & 3 & 4 & 5 & 6 \end{pmatrix};$$
rotation about the centre through $2\pi/3$ anticlockwise,
$$\begin{pmatrix} 1 & 2 & 3 & 4 & 5 & 6 \\ 3 & 4 & 5 & 6 & 1 & 2 \end{pmatrix};$$
rotation about the centre through $4\pi/3$ anticlockwise,
$$\begin{pmatrix} 1 & 2 & 3 & 4 & 5 & 6 \\ 5 & 6 & 1 & 2 & 3 & 4 \end{pmatrix};$$
reflection in the line bisecting the edges joining the locations $1, 6$ and $3, 4$,
$$\begin{pmatrix} 1 & 2 & 3 & 4 & 5 & 6 \\ 6 & 5 & 4 & 3 & 2 & 1 \end{pmatrix};$$
reflection in the line bisecting the edges joining the locations $2, 3$ and $5, 6$,
$$\begin{pmatrix} 1 & 2 & 3 & 4 & 5 & 6 \\ 4 & 3 & 2 & 1 & 6 & 5 \end{pmatrix};$$
reflection in the line bisecting the edges joining the locations $4, 5$ and $1, 2$,
$$\begin{pmatrix} 1 & 2 & 3 & 4 & 5 & 6 \\ 2 & 1 & 6 & 5 & 4 & 3 \end{pmatrix}.$$

2.10 (a)

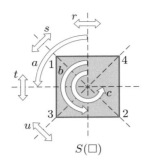

$S(\square)$

The two-line symbols are

$$e = \begin{pmatrix} 1 & 2 & 3 & 4 \\ 1 & 2 & 3 & 4 \end{pmatrix}, \quad a = \begin{pmatrix} 1 & 2 & 3 & 4 \\ 3 & 4 & 2 & 1 \end{pmatrix},$$

$$b = \begin{pmatrix} 1 & 2 & 3 & 4 \\ 2 & 1 & 4 & 3 \end{pmatrix}, \quad c = \begin{pmatrix} 1 & 2 & 3 & 4 \\ 4 & 3 & 1 & 2 \end{pmatrix},$$

$$r = \begin{pmatrix} 1 & 2 & 3 & 4 \\ 4 & 3 & 2 & 1 \end{pmatrix}, \quad s = \begin{pmatrix} 1 & 2 & 3 & 4 \\ 1 & 2 & 4 & 3 \end{pmatrix},$$

$$t = \begin{pmatrix} 1 & 2 & 3 & 4 \\ 3 & 4 & 1 & 2 \end{pmatrix}, \quad u = \begin{pmatrix} 1 & 2 & 3 & 4 \\ 2 & 1 & 3 & 4 \end{pmatrix}.$$

(b)

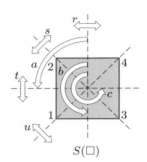

$S(\square)$

The two-line symbols are

$$e = \begin{pmatrix} 1 & 2 & 3 & 4 \\ 1 & 2 & 3 & 4 \end{pmatrix}, \quad a = \begin{pmatrix} 1 & 2 & 3 & 4 \\ 3 & 1 & 4 & 2 \end{pmatrix},$$

$$b = \begin{pmatrix} 1 & 2 & 3 & 4 \\ 4 & 3 & 2 & 1 \end{pmatrix}, \quad c = \begin{pmatrix} 1 & 2 & 3 & 4 \\ 2 & 4 & 1 & 3 \end{pmatrix},$$

$$r = \begin{pmatrix} 1 & 2 & 3 & 4 \\ 3 & 4 & 1 & 2 \end{pmatrix}, \quad s = \begin{pmatrix} 1 & 2 & 3 & 4 \\ 4 & 2 & 3 & 1 \end{pmatrix},$$

$$t = \begin{pmatrix} 1 & 2 & 3 & 4 \\ 2 & 1 & 4 & 3 \end{pmatrix}, \quad u = \begin{pmatrix} 1 & 2 & 3 & 4 \\ 1 & 3 & 2 & 4 \end{pmatrix}.$$

2.11 The two-line symbols are

$$e = \begin{pmatrix} 1 & 2 & 3 & 4 \\ 1 & 2 & 3 & 4 \end{pmatrix}, \quad a = \begin{pmatrix} 1 & 2 & 3 & 4 \\ 3 & 4 & 1 & 2 \end{pmatrix},$$

$$r = \begin{pmatrix} 1 & 2 & 3 & 4 \\ 1 & 4 & 3 & 2 \end{pmatrix}, \quad s = \begin{pmatrix} 1 & 2 & 3 & 4 \\ 3 & 2 & 1 & 4 \end{pmatrix}.$$

2.12

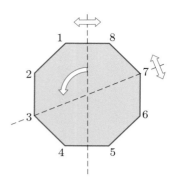

(a) $\begin{pmatrix} 1 & 2 & 3 & 4 & 5 & 6 & 7 & 8 \\ 3 & 4 & 5 & 6 & 7 & 8 & 1 & 2 \end{pmatrix}$ represents anticlockwise rotation through $\pi/2$ about the centre.

(b) $\begin{pmatrix} 1 & 2 & 3 & 4 & 5 & 6 & 7 & 8 \\ 8 & 7 & 6 & 5 & 4 & 3 & 2 & 1 \end{pmatrix}$ represents reflection in the axis bisecting the edges joining locations $1, 8$ and $4, 5$.

(c) $\begin{pmatrix} 1 & 2 & 3 & 4 & 5 & 6 & 7 & 8 \\ 5 & 4 & 3 & 2 & 1 & 8 & 7 & 6 \end{pmatrix}$ represents reflection in the axis joining locations 3 and 7.

2.13 The two-line symbols are

$$x \circ x = \begin{pmatrix} 1 & 2 & 3 \\ 3 & 1 & 2 \end{pmatrix} \circ \begin{pmatrix} 1 & 2 & 3 \\ 3 & 1 & 2 \end{pmatrix} = \begin{pmatrix} 1 & 2 & 3 \\ 2 & 3 & 1 \end{pmatrix},$$

$$y \circ y = \begin{pmatrix} 1 & 2 & 3 \\ 3 & 2 & 1 \end{pmatrix} \circ \begin{pmatrix} 1 & 2 & 3 \\ 3 & 2 & 1 \end{pmatrix}$$
$$= \begin{pmatrix} 1 & 2 & 3 \\ 1 & 2 & 3 \end{pmatrix} = e,$$

$$x \circ y = \begin{pmatrix} 1 & 2 & 3 \\ 3 & 1 & 2 \end{pmatrix} \circ \begin{pmatrix} 1 & 2 & 3 \\ 3 & 2 & 1 \end{pmatrix} = \begin{pmatrix} 1 & 2 & 3 \\ 2 & 1 & 3 \end{pmatrix},$$

$$y \circ x = \begin{pmatrix} 1 & 2 & 3 \\ 3 & 2 & 1 \end{pmatrix} \circ \begin{pmatrix} 1 & 2 & 3 \\ 3 & 1 & 2 \end{pmatrix} = \begin{pmatrix} 1 & 2 & 3 \\ 1 & 3 & 2 \end{pmatrix}.$$

Using the above results, we obtain

$$(x \circ x) \circ x = \begin{pmatrix} 1 & 2 & 3 \\ 2 & 3 & 1 \end{pmatrix} \circ \begin{pmatrix} 1 & 2 & 3 \\ 3 & 1 & 2 \end{pmatrix}$$
$$= \begin{pmatrix} 1 & 2 & 3 \\ 1 & 2 & 3 \end{pmatrix} = e,$$

$$(x \circ x) \circ y = \begin{pmatrix} 1 & 2 & 3 \\ 2 & 3 & 1 \end{pmatrix} \circ \begin{pmatrix} 1 & 2 & 3 \\ 3 & 2 & 1 \end{pmatrix}$$
$$= \begin{pmatrix} 1 & 2 & 3 \\ 1 & 3 & 2 \end{pmatrix} = y \circ x,$$

$$y \circ (x \circ x) = \begin{pmatrix} 1 & 2 & 3 \\ 3 & 2 & 1 \end{pmatrix} \circ \begin{pmatrix} 1 & 2 & 3 \\ 2 & 3 & 1 \end{pmatrix}$$
$$= \begin{pmatrix} 1 & 2 & 3 \\ 2 & 1 & 3 \end{pmatrix} = x \circ y.$$

3.1 (a) $(\mathbb{R}, +)$ is a group. The proof is similar to the proof in Frame 3.

We show that the four group axioms hold.

G1　For all $x, y \in \mathbb{R}$,
$$x + y \in \mathbb{R},$$
so $\mathbb{R}$ is closed under $+$.

G2　For all $x \in \mathbb{R}$,
$$x + 0 = x = 0 + x,$$
and $0 \in \mathbb{R}$, so 0 is an identity element.

G3　For each $x \in \mathbb{R}$,
$$x + (-x) = 0 = (-x) + x,$$
and $-x \in \mathbb{R}$, so $-x$ is an inverse of x.

G4　Addition of real numbers is associative.

Hence $(\mathbb{R}, +)$ satisfies the four group axioms, and so is a group.

(b) $(\mathbb{Q}, \times)$ is not a group. This situation is similar to that in Frame 4.

Axioms G1 and G2 hold, and 1 is a multiplicative identity, but axiom G3 fails because 0 has no multiplicative inverse in $\mathbb{Q}$.

(c) $(\mathbb{Q}^*, \times)$ is a group. The proof is similar to the proof in Frame 5.

We show that the four group axioms hold.

G1　For all $x, y \in \mathbb{Q}^*$, we have $x \neq 0$ and $y \neq 0$, so $x \times y \neq 0$ and $x \times y \in \mathbb{Q}^*$, so $\mathbb{Q}^*$ is closed under $\times$.

G2　For all $x \in \mathbb{Q}^*$,
$$x \times 1 = x = 1 \times x,$$
and $1 \in \mathbb{Q}^*$, so 1 is an identity element.

G3　For each $x \in \mathbb{Q}^*$, we have $x \neq 0$, so $1/x$ is defined and is non-zero; hence $1/x \in \mathbb{Q}^*$. Also,
$$x \times \frac{1}{x} = 1 = \frac{1}{x} \times x,$$
so $1/x$ is an inverse of x.

G4　Multiplication of rational numbers is associative.

Hence $(\mathbb{Q}^*, \times)$ satisfies the four group axioms, and so is a group.

3.2 (a) $(\mathbb{Z}, \times)$ is not a group.

$\mathbb{Z}$ is closed under multiplication, and 1 is a multiplicative identity, so axioms G1 and G2 hold.

However, axiom G3 fails because, for example, 2 has no multiplicative inverse in $\mathbb{Z}$, since $\frac{1}{2} \notin \mathbb{Z}$.

(b) $(\mathbb{Z}, -)$ is not a group.

$\mathbb{Z}$ is closed under subtraction, but there is no identity element; for example, there is no integer n such that
$$2 - n = 2 = n - 2,$$
so axiom G2 fails.

Alternatively, we can show that axiom G4 fails using the argument given in Frame 8, part (i). The integers 6, 4 and 1 belong to $\mathbb{Z}$, and
$$6 - (4 - 1) = 6 - 3 = 3,$$
but
$$(6 - 4) - 1 = 2 - 1 = 1.$$
Since $3 \neq 1$, subtraction is not associative on $\mathbb{Z}$.

(c) $(G = \{\text{odd integers}\}, \times)$ is not a group.

The product of two odd integers is odd, so G is closed under $\times$. Also, 1 is odd, so 1 is a multiplicative identity. So axioms G1 and G2 hold.

However, axiom G3 fails because, for example, 3 has no multiplicative inverse in G, since $\frac{1}{3} \notin G$.

(d) $(2\pi\mathbb{Z}, +)$ is a group.

We show that the four group axioms hold.

G1　For all $m, n \in \mathbb{Z}$,
$$2\pi m + 2\pi n = 2\pi(m + n) \in 2\pi\mathbb{Z},$$
so $2\pi\mathbb{Z}$ is closed under $+$.

G2　For all $k \in \mathbb{Z}$,
$$2\pi k + 0 = 2\pi k = 0 + 2\pi k,$$
and $0 = 2\pi \times 0 \in 2\pi\mathbb{Z}$, so 0 is an identity element.

G3　For each $k \in \mathbb{Z}$,
$$2\pi k + 2\pi(-k) = 0 = 2\pi(-k) + 2\pi k,$$
and $2\pi(-k) \in 2\pi\mathbb{Z}$, so $2\pi(-k)$ is an inverse of $2\pi k$.

G4　Addition is associative on $2\pi\mathbb{Z}$.

Hence $(2\pi\mathbb{Z}, +)$ satisfies the four group axioms, and so is a group.

(e) Here the operation is unfamiliar, so we examine the axioms in turn.

The approach is similar to that in Frame 9.

G1　For all $x, y \in \mathbb{R}$,
$$x \circ y = x - y - 1 \in \mathbb{R},$$
so $\mathbb{R}$ is closed under $\circ$.

G2　Is there an identity element $e \in \mathbb{R}$ such that, for each $x \in \mathbb{R}$,
$$x \circ e = x = e \circ x?$$
That is, is there a real number e such that
$$x - e - 1 = x = e - x - 1?$$
Clearly, there is not because
$$x - e - 1 = x \Rightarrow e = -1$$
and
$$e - x - 1 = x \Rightarrow e = 2x + 1.$$
Thus, for each $x \in \mathbb{R}$, we must have
$$e = -1 = 2x + 1.$$
But this is false for $x = 0$, for example, so axiom G2 fails.

Hence $(\mathbb{R}, \circ)$ is not a group.

3.3 (a) Let $x, y, z \in \mathbb{R}$. Then

$x \circ (y \circ z)$

$= x \circ (y + z - yz)$

$= x + (y + z - yz) - x(y + z - yz)$

$= x + y + z - xy - xz - yz + xyz$ $\qquad$ (S.1)

and

$(x \circ y) \circ z$

$= (x + y - xy) \circ z$

$= (x + y - xy) + z - (x + y - xy)z$

$= x + y + z - xy - xz - yz + xyz.$ $\qquad$ (S.2)

Expressions (S.1) and (S.2) are the same, so $\circ$ is associative on $\mathbb{R}$.

(b) Let $x, y, z \in \mathbb{R}$. Then

$x \circ (y \circ z)$

$= x \circ (y - z + yz)$

$= x - (y - z + yz) + x(y - z + yz)$

$= x - y + z + xy - xz - yz + xyz$ $\qquad$ (S.3)

and

$(x \circ y) \circ z$

$= (x - y + xy) \circ z$

$= (x - y + xy) - z + (x - y + xy)z$

$= x - y - z + xy + xz - yz + xyz.$ $\qquad$ (S.4)

Expressions (S.3) and (S.4) are not the same.
For example, if $x = 0$, $y = 1$ and $z = 2$, then

$0 \circ (1 \circ 2) = 0 \circ (1 - 2 + 2)$

$\qquad\qquad = 0 \circ 1$

$\qquad\qquad = 0 - 1 + 0 = -1$

but

$(0 \circ 1) \circ 2 = (0 - 1 + 0) \circ 2$

$\qquad\qquad = (-1) \circ 2$

$\qquad\qquad = -1 - 2 - 2 = -5,$

so $\circ$ is not associative on $\mathbb{R}$.

(If you can see that $\circ$ is not associative, then it is not necessary to calculate expressions (S.3) and (S.4)); it is sufficient to produce a specific counter-example.)

3.4 We show that $(\mathbb{R} - \{-1\}, \circ)$ satisfies the group axioms.

The proof of axiom G1 needs care.

G1 $\quad$ For all $x, y \in \mathbb{R} - \{-1\}$,

$\qquad x \circ y = x + y + xy \in \mathbb{R}.$

To show that $x + y + xy \in \mathbb{R} - \{-1\}$, we need to show that, for all $x, y \in \mathbb{R} - \{-1\}$,

$\qquad x + y + xy \neq -1.$

Now, if $x, y \in \mathbb{R}$, and

$\qquad x + y + xy = -1,$

then

$\qquad x(1 + y) = -(1 + y).$

So EITHER $x = -1$, OR $1 + y = 0$, so $y = -1$. However, the given set does not contain -1, so neither of these conclusions is possible. Thus $x \circ y$ cannot equal -1.

Hence, if $x, y \in \mathbb{R} - \{-1\}$, then $x \circ y \in \mathbb{R} - \{-1\}$, so $\mathbb{R} - \{-1\}$ is closed under $\circ$.

G2 $\quad$ In Frame 9 we showed that 0 is an identity element for $\circ$ on $\mathbb{R}$, and $0 \in \mathbb{R} - \{-1\}$, so 0 is an identity element for $\circ$ on $\mathbb{R} - \{-1\}$.

G3 $\quad$ In Frame 9 we showed that, for each element x in $\mathbb{R} - \{-1\}$, $x \circ y = e$, where $y = -x/(1 + x)$. Here, $x \neq 1 + x$, so $y \neq -1$. Also, $x \circ y = y \circ x$, so each element x in $\mathbb{R} - \{-1\}$ has an inverse $-x/(1 + x)$ in $\mathbb{R} - \{-1\}$.

G4 $\quad$ Let $x, y, z \in \mathbb{R} - \{-1\}$. Our working in Frame 8 shows that $\circ$ is associative on $\mathbb{R} - \{-1\}$.

Hence $(\mathbb{R} - \{-1\}, \circ)$ satisfies the four group axioms, and so is a group.

3.5 (a) This situation is similar to that in Frame 11.

The Cayley table for $(\mathbb{Z}_5, +_5)$ is as follows.

$+_5$	0	1	2	3	4
0	0	1	2	3	4
1	1	2	3	4	0
2	2	3	4	0	1
3	3	4	0	1	2
4	4	0	1	2	3

We show that the four group axioms hold.

G1 $\quad$ No new elements are needed to complete the table, so $\mathbb{Z}_5$ is closed under $+_5$.

G2 $\quad$ The first row of the table shows that

$\qquad 0 +_5 x = x, \quad$ for each $x \in \mathbb{Z}_5$.

The first column of the table shows that

$\qquad x +_5 0 = x, \quad$ for each $x \in \mathbb{Z}_5$.

Hence 0 is an identity element.

G3 $\quad$ From the Cayley table above, we see that

$\qquad 0 +_5 0 = 0,$

$\qquad 1 +_5 4 = 0 = 4 +_5 1,$

$\qquad 2 +_5 3 = 0 = 3 +_5 2,$

so

$\qquad$ 0 is self-inverse,

$\qquad$ 1 and 4 are inverses of each other,

$\qquad$ 2 and 3 are inverses of each other.

G4 $\quad$ The operation $+_5$ is associative.

Hence $(\mathbb{Z}_5, +_5)$ satisfies the four group axioms, and so is a group.

(b) This situation is similar to that in Frame 12.

The Cayley table for $(\mathbb{Z}_5, \times_5)$ is as follows.

$\times_5$	0	1	2	3	4
0	0	0	0	0	0
1	0	1	2	3	4
2	0	2	4	1	3
3	0	3	1	4	2
4	0	4	3	2	1

Axioms G1 and G2 hold, and 1 is an identity element.

However, there is no 1 in the column labelled 0, so 0 has no inverse, so axiom G3 fails.

Hence $(\mathbb{Z}_5, \times_5)$ is not a group.

(c) In this case, the troublesome 0 has been omitted, and the Cayley table is as follows.

$\times_5$	1	2	3	4
1	1	2	3	4
2	2	4	1	3
3	3	1	4	2
4	4	3	2	1

We check the four group axioms in turn.

G1 No new elements are needed to complete the table, so $\mathbb{Z}_5^*$ is closed under $\times_5$.

G2 The first row of the table shows that
$$1 \times_5 x = x, \quad \text{for each } x \in \mathbb{Z}_5^*.$$
The first column of the table shows that
$$x \times_5 1 = x, \quad \text{for each } x \in \mathbb{Z}_5^*.$$
Hence 1 is an identity element.

G3 From the table, we see that
$$1 \times_5 1 = 1,$$
$$4 \times_5 4 = 1,$$
$$2 \times_5 3 = 1 = 3 \times_5 2,$$
so

1 and 4 are self-inverse,

2 and 3 are inverses of each other.

G4 The operation $\times_5$ is associative.

Hence $(\mathbb{Z}_5^*, \times_5)$ satisfies the four group axioms, and so is a group.

3.6 (a) This situation is similar to that in Frame 11, and to Exercise 3.5(a).

The Cayley table for $(\mathbb{Z}_6, +_6)$ is as follows.

$+_6$	0	1	2	3	4	5
0	0	1	2	3	4	5
1	1	2	3	4	5	0
2	2	3	4	5	0	1
3	3	4	5	0	1	2
4	4	5	0	1	2	3
5	5	0	1	2	3	4

We check the four group axioms in turn.

G1 No new elements are needed to complete the table, so $\mathbb{Z}_6$ is closed under $+_6$.

G2 The row and column labelled 0 repeat the borders of the table, so 0 is an identity.

G3 From the table, we see that each element has an inverse in $\mathbb{Z}_6$.

Element	0	1	2	3	4	5
Inverse	0	5	4	3	2	1

G4 The operation $+_6$ is associative.

Hence $(\mathbb{Z}_6, +_6)$ satisfies the four group axioms, and so is a group.

(b) This situation is similar to that in Frame 12, and to Exercise 3.5(b).

The Cayley table for $(\mathbb{Z}_6, \times_6)$ is as follows.

$\times_6$	0	1	2	3	4	5
0	0	0	0	0	0	0
1	0	1	2	3	4	5
2	0	2	4	0	2	4
3	0	3	0	3	0	3
4	0	4	2	0	4	2
5	0	5	4	3	2	1

Axioms G1 and G2 hold, and 1 is an identity.

However, there is no 1 in the column labelled 0, so 0 has no inverse, and axiom G3 fails.

Hence $(\mathbb{Z}_6, \times_6)$ is not a group.

(c) The Cayley table for $(\mathbb{Z}_7^*, \times_7)$ is as follows.

$\times_7$	1	2	3	4	5	6
1	1	2	3	4	5	6
2	2	4	6	1	3	5
3	3	6	2	5	1	4
4	4	1	5	2	6	3
5	5	3	1	6	4	2
6	6	5	4	3	2	1

We check the four group axioms in turn.

G1 No new elements are needed to complete the table, so $\mathbb{Z}_7^*$ is closed under $\times_7$.

G2 The row and column labelled 1 repeat the borders of the table, so 1 is an identity.

G3 From the table, we see that each element has an inverse in $\mathbb{Z}_7^*$.

Element	1	2	3	4	5	6
Inverse	1	4	5	2	3	6

G4 The operation $\times_7$ is associative.

Hence $(\mathbb{Z}_7^*, \times_7)$ satisfies the four group axioms, and so is a group.

(d) The Cayley table for $(\{1, -1\}, \times)$ is as follows.

$\times$	1	-1
1	1	-1
-1	-1	1

We check the four group axioms in turn.

G1   No new elements are needed to complete the table, so $\{1, -1\}$ is closed under $\times$.

G2   From the table, we see that 1 is an identity element.

G3   Since $1 \times 1 = 1$ and $(-1) \times (-1) = 1$, 1 and -1 are both self-inverse.

G4   Multiplication of numbers is associative.

Hence $(\{1, -1\}, \times)$ satisfies the four group axioms, and so is a group.

3.7 We show that the four group axioms hold.

G1   For all $a, b \in \mathbb{Q}^+$, we have $a \circ b = \frac{1}{2}ab \in \mathbb{Q}^+$, so $\mathbb{Q}^+$ is closed under the operation $\circ$.

G2   For all $a \in \mathbb{Q}^+$,
$$a \circ 2 = a = 2 \circ a,$$
and $2 \in \mathbb{Q}^+$, so 2 is an identity element.

G3   An inverse of a is not obvious, so we assume that an inverse x exists, and try to find it.
We seek $x \in \mathbb{Q}^+$ such that
$$a \circ x = 2 = x \circ a;$$
that is,
$$\tfrac{1}{2}ax = 2 = \tfrac{1}{2}xa,$$
so the only possibility is $x = 4/a$.
For each $a \in \mathbb{Q}^+$, we have $4/a \in \mathbb{Q}^+$, so $4/a$ is an inverse of a.

G4   For all $a, b, c \in \mathbb{Q}^+$,
$$\begin{aligned} a \circ (b \circ c) &= a \circ (\tfrac{1}{2}bc) \\ &= \tfrac{1}{2}a(\tfrac{1}{2}bc) \\ &= \tfrac{1}{4}abc \end{aligned} \tag{S.5}$$
and
$$\begin{aligned} (a \circ b) \circ c &= (\tfrac{1}{2}ab) \circ c \\ &= \tfrac{1}{2}(\tfrac{1}{2}ab)c \\ &= \tfrac{1}{4}abc. \end{aligned} \tag{S.6}$$
Expressions (S.5) and (S.6) are the same, so $\circ$ is associative on $\mathbb{Q}^+$.

Hence $(\mathbb{Q}^+, \circ)$ satisfies the four group axioms, and so is a group.

3.8 (a) $(\mathbb{C}, +)$ is a group. The proof is similar to the proof in Frame 3.

We show that the four group axioms hold.

G1   For all $x, y \in \mathbb{C}$,
$$x + y \in \mathbb{C},$$
so $\mathbb{C}$ is closed under $+$.

G2   For all $x \in \mathbb{C}$,
$$x + 0 = x = 0 + x,$$
and $0 \in \mathbb{C}$, so 0 is an identity element.

G3   For each $x \in \mathbb{C}$,
$$x + (-x) = 0 = (-x) + x,$$
and $-x \in \mathbb{C}$, so $-x$ is an inverse of x.

G4   Addition of complex numbers is associative.

Hence $(\mathbb{C}, +)$ satisfies the four group axioms, and so is a group.

3.9 We show that the four group axioms hold.

G1   For all integers $m, n \in \mathbb{Z}$,
$$2m + 2n = 2(m + n) \in 2\mathbb{Z},$$
so $2\mathbb{Z}$ is closed under $+$.

G2   For all $k \in \mathbb{Z}$,
$$2k + 0 = 2k = 0 + 2k,$$
and $0 = 2 \times 0 \in 2\mathbb{Z}$, so 0 is an identity in $2\mathbb{Z}$.

G3   For each $k \in \mathbb{Z}$,
$$2k + (-2k) = 0 = (-2k) + 2k,$$
and $-2k = 2(-k) \in 2\mathbb{Z}$, so $-2k$ is an inverse of $2k$ in $2\mathbb{Z}$.

G4   Addition of integers is associative.

Hence $(2\mathbb{Z}, +)$ satisfies the four group axioms, and so is a group.

3.10 We show that the four group axioms hold.

G1   For all $m, n \in \mathbb{Z}$,
$$2^m \times 2^n = 2^{m+n} \in G,$$
so G is closed under $\times$.

G2   For all $k \in \mathbb{Z}$,
$$2^k \times 2^0 = 2^k = 2^0 \times 2^k,$$
and $2^0 = 1 \in G$, so 1 is an identity in G.

G3   For each $k \in \mathbb{Z}$,
$$2^k \times 2^{-k} = 2^{k-k} = 1 = 2^{-k+k} = 2^{-k} \times 2^k,$$
so 2^{-k} is an inverse of 2^k in G.

G4 For all $k, m, n \in \mathbb{Z}$,
$$2^k \times (2^m \times 2^n) = 2^k \times 2^{m+n}$$
$$= 2^{k+(m+n)}$$
$$= 2^{k+m+n} \qquad \text{(S.7)}$$
and
$$(2^k \times 2^m) \times 2^n = 2^{k+m} \times 2^n$$
$$= 2^{(k+m)+n}$$
$$= 2^{k+m+n}. \qquad \text{(S.8)}$$

Expressions (S.7) and (S.8) are the same, so $\times$ is associative on G.

Hence $(G, \times)$ satisfies the four group axioms, and so is a group.

3.11 In each case, we begin by completing a Cayley table, and then examine the group axioms.

(a)

$\times_8$	1	3	5	7
1	1	3	5	7
3	3	1	7	5
5	5	7	1	3
7	7	5	3	1

G1 No new elements are needed to complete the table, so $\{1, 3, 5, 7\}$ is closed under $\times_8$.

G2 From the table, we see that 1 is an identity, and $1 \in \{1, 3, 5, 7\}$.

G3 From the table, we see that each element in $\{1, 3, 5, 7\}$ is self-inverse, so this set contains an inverse of each element.

G4 Multiplication of numbers is associative.

Hence $(\{1, 3, 5, 7\}, \times_8)$ satisfies the four group axioms, and so is a group.

(b)

$\times_{15}$	1	2	4	7	8	11	13	14
1	1	2	4	7	8	11	13	14
2	2	4	8	14	1	7	11	13
4	4	8	1	13	2	14	7	11
7	7	14	13	4	11	2	1	8
8	8	1	2	11	4	13	14	7
11	11	7	14	2	13	1	8	4
13	13	11	7	1	14	8	4	2
14	14	13	11	8	7	4	2	1

G1 No new elements are needed to complete the table, so $\{1, 2, 4, 7, 8, 11, 13, 14\}$ is closed under $\times_{15}$.

G2 From the table, we see that 1 is an identity, and $1 \in \{1, 2, 4, 7, 8, 11, 13, 14\}$.

G3 From the table, we see that each element has an inverse in the set.

Element	1	2	4	7	8	11	13	14
Inverse	1	8	4	13	2	11	7	14

G4 Multiplication of numbers is associative.

Hence $(\{1, 2, 4, 7, 8, 11, 13, 14\}, \times_{15})$ satisfies the four group axioms, and so is a group.

(c)

$\times_{15}$	1	4	11	14
1	1	4	11	14
4	4	1	14	11
11	11	14	1	4
14	14	11	4	1

G1 No new elements are needed to complete the table, so $\{1, 4, 11, 14\}$ is closed under $\times_{15}$.

G2 From the table, we see that 1 is an identity, and $1 \in \{1, 4, 11, 14\}$.

G3 From the table, we see that each element in $\{1, 4, 11, 14\}$ is self-inverse, so each element has an inverse in the set.

G4 Multiplication of numbers is associative.

Hence $(\{1, 4, 11, 14\}, \times_{15})$ satisfies the four group axioms, and so is a group.

(d)

$+_{10}$	0	2	4	6	8
0	0	2	4	6	8
2	2	4	6	8	0
4	4	6	8	0	2
6	6	8	0	2	4
8	8	0	2	4	6

G1 No new elements are needed to complete the table, so $\{0, 2, 4, 6, 8\}$ is closed under $+_{10}$.

G2 From the table, we see that 0 is an identity element, and $0 \in \{0, 2, 4, 6, 8\}$.

G3 From the table, we see that each element has an inverse in the set.

Element	0	2	4	6	8
Inverse	0	8	6	4	2

G4 Addition of numbers is associative.

Hence $(\{0, 2, 4, 6, 8\}, +_{10})$ satisfies the four group axioms, and so is a group.

3.12 (a) $(\mathbb{Z}_9^*, \times_9)$ is not a group.

The operation $\times_9$ is not closed on the set $\mathbb{Z}_9^* = \{1, 2, 3, 4, 5, 6, 7, 8\}$ because, for example, $3 \in \mathbb{Z}_9^*$ and $6 \in \mathbb{Z}_9^*$, but $3 \times_9 6 = 0 \notin \mathbb{Z}_9^*$, so axiom G1 fails.

(b) $(\mathbb{Z}_9, +_9)$ is a group.

The Cayley table is as follows.

$+_9$	0	1	2	3	4	5	6	7	8
0	0	1	2	3	4	5	6	7	8
1	1	2	3	4	5	6	7	8	0
2	2	3	4	5	6	7	8	0	1
3	3	4	5	6	7	8	0	1	2
4	4	5	6	7	8	0	1	2	3
5	5	6	7	8	0	1	2	3	4
6	6	7	8	0	1	2	3	4	5
7	7	8	0	1	2	3	4	5	6
8	8	0	1	2	3	4	5	6	7

G1 No new elements are needed to complete the table, so $\mathbb{Z}_9$ is closed under $+_9$.

G2 From the table, we see that 0 is an identity element, and $0 \in \mathbb{Z}_9$.

G3 From the table, we see that each element has an inverse in the set.

Element	0	1	2	3	4	5	6	7	8
Inverse	0	8	7	6	5	4	3	2	1

G4 Addition of numbers is associative.

Hence $(\mathbb{Z}_9, +_9)$ satisfies the four group axioms, and so is a group.

(c) $(\mathbb{Z}_{11}^*, \times_{11})$ is a group.

The Cayley table is as follows.

$\times_{11}$	1	2	3	4	5	6	7	8	9	10
1	1	2	3	4	5	6	7	8	9	10
2	2	4	6	8	10	1	3	5	7	9
3	3	6	9	1	4	7	10	2	5	8
4	4	8	1	5	9	2	6	10	3	7
5	5	10	4	9	3	8	2	7	1	6
6	6	1	7	2	8	3	9	4	10	5
7	7	3	10	6	2	9	5	1	8	4
8	8	5	2	10	7	4	1	9	6	3
9	9	7	5	3	1	10	8	6	4	2
10	10	9	8	7	6	5	4	3	2	1

G1 No new elements are needed to complete the table, so $\mathbb{Z}_{11}^*$ is closed under $\times_{11}$.

G2 From the table, we see that 1 is an identity, and $1 \in \mathbb{Z}_{11}^*$.

G3 From the table, we see that each element has an inverse in the set.

Element	1	2	3	4	5	6	7	8	9	10
Inverse	1	6	4	3	9	2	8	7	5	10

G4 Multiplication of numbers is associative.

Hence $(\mathbb{Z}_{11}^*, \times_{11})$ satisfies the four group axioms, and so is a group.

4.1 (a) The second row and the second column repeat the borders of the table, so the identity is E.

(Here the letters E and O could denote the sets of even and odd integers under addition.)

(b) The first row and the first column repeat the borders of the table, so the identity is D.

(Here the letters D and I could denote the sets of direct and indirect symmetries of a figure with rotational and reflectional symmetries under composition.)

(c) The third row and the third column repeat the borders of the table, so the identity is w.

4.2 The fifth row and the fifth column repeat the borders of the table, so the identity is e.

The table of inverses is as follows.

Element	a	b	c	d	e	f	g	h
Inverse	b	a	d	c	e	f	h	g

4.3 The elements a, b and c do not have inverses.

For example, from row 2 we see that the only possible candidate for a^{-1} is c, since $a \circ c = e$; but from row 4 we see that $c \circ a = d \neq e$, so a has no inverse.

Alternatively, the element e does not appear symmetrically about the main diagonal.

4.4 (a) Suppose that, in a group $(G, \circ)$,
$$x \circ a = x \circ b.$$
The element x has an inverse x^{-1} in G, so composing both sides on the left with x^{-1}, we obtain
$$x^{-1} \circ (x \circ a) = x^{-1} \circ (x \circ b).$$
Hence
$$(x^{-1} \circ x) \circ a = (x^{-1} \circ x) \circ b \quad \text{(associativity).}$$
But
$$x^{-1} \circ x = e \quad \text{(inverses),}$$
so we have
$$e \circ a = e \circ b,$$
and hence
$$a = b \quad \text{(identity).}$$

(b) Similarly, if
$$a \circ x = b \circ x,$$
then, composing both sides on the right with x^{-1}, we obtain
$$(a \circ x) \circ x^{-1} = (b \circ x) \circ x^{-1},$$
so
$$a \circ (x \circ x^{-1}) = b \circ (x \circ x^{-1}) \quad \text{(associativity).}$$
Hence
$$a \circ e = b \circ e \quad \text{(inverses),}$$
so
$$a = b \quad \text{(identity).}$$

4.5 (a) The table of inverses is as follows.

Element	e	a	b	c	d	f	g	h
Inverse	e	a	b	c	d	f	g	h

The group table is symmetrical about the leading diagonal, so this group is Abelian.

(b) The table of inverses is as follows.

Element	e	a	b	c	d	f	g	h
Inverse	e	c	b	a	g	h	d	f

The group is non-Abelian; for example, $a \circ d = f$, but $d \circ a = h$.

4.6 We use the property that in a group table each element must appear once in each row and once in each column.

(a)

	e	a	b
e	e	a	b
a	a	b	e
b	b	e	a

(b)

	a	b	c	d
a	a	b	c	d
b	b	c	d	a
c	c	d	a	b
d	d	a	b	c

4.7 (a) The first row and the first column repeat the borders of the table, so the identity is e.

(b) The table of inverses is as follows.

Element	e	a	b	c	d	f	g	h
Inverse	e	c	b	a	h	g	f	d

(c) The group is non-Abelian because the table is not symmetrical about the leading diagonal; for example, $h \circ g = c$, whereas $g \circ h = a$.

4.8 (a) The operation $\circ$ is not closed: a new element d occurs in the body of the table, so axiom G1 fails.

(b) Here the operation $\circ$ is closed, and we see from row 2 and column 2 that a is an identity element.

However, a does not occur symmetrically about the main diagonal, so this is not a group.

Alternatively, in row 1 and column 3, b occurs twice so this is not a group.

(c) Again, the operation $\circ$ is closed, and we see from row 1 and column 1 that e is an identity element.

However, e does not appear symmetrically about the main diagonal, so this is not a group.

Alternatively, the operation is not associative because

$$a \circ (b \circ d) = a \circ a = b$$

but

$$(a \circ b) \circ d = d \circ d = e.$$

Hence

$$a \circ (b \circ d) \neq (a \circ b) \circ d,$$

so axiom G4 fails.

(d) Here the only axiom that fails is G4; for example,

$$a \circ (b \circ d) = a \circ f = d$$

but

$$(a \circ b) \circ d = f \circ d = e.$$

Hence

$$a \circ (b \circ d) \neq (a \circ b) \circ d,$$

so axiom G4 fails.

4.9 We know that $|G|$ is even and that, for each element $g \in G$,

EITHER $\quad g$ is self-inverse

OR $\qquad g$ and g^{-1} are distinct elements which are inverses of each other.

It follows that the number of elements which are self-inverse must be even.

However, e is self-inverse, so there must be at least one element $g \in G$ such that

$$g \circ g = e \quad \text{and} \quad g \neq e.$$

5.1 In each case, we use Strategy 5.1.

Cube

The cube has 6 faces.

Each face of the cube is a square, and so has 8 symmetries (since the order of $S(\square)$ is 8).

It follows from the strategy that the number of symmetries of the cube is $6 \times 8 = 48$.

Octahedron

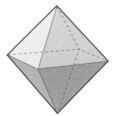

The octahedron has 8 faces.

Each face of the octahedron is an equilateral triangle, and so has 6 symmetries (since the order of $S(\triangle)$ is 6).

It follows from the strategy that the number of symmetries of the octahedron is $8 \times 6 = 48$.

Dodecahedron

The dodecahedron has 12 faces.

Each face of the dodecahedron is a regular pentagon, and so has 10 symmetries (since the order of $S(\bigcirc)$ is 10).

It follows from the strategy that the number of symmetries of the dodecahedron is $12 \times 10 = 120$.

Icosahedron

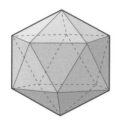

The icosahedron has 20 faces.

Each face of the icosahedron is an equilateral triangle, and so has 6 symmetries.

It follows from the strategy that the number of symmetries of the icosahedron is $20 \times 6 = 120$.

5.2 We use Strategy 5.2.

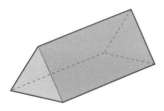

The triangular prism has two (congruent) equilateral triangle faces and three (congruent) rectangular faces; so there are two ways of applying the strategy.

Consider the equilateral triangle faces.

1. The prism has 2 (congruent) equilateral triangle faces.

2. Each triangular face is an equilateral triangle, and so has 6 symmetries; each of these symmetries is also a symmetry of the whole prism.

It follows from the strategy that the number of symmetries of the triangular prism is $2 \times 6 = 12$.

Alternatively, consider the rectangular faces.

1. The prism has 3 (congruent) rectangular faces.

2. Each rectangular face has 4 symmetries (since $S(\square)$ has order 4); each of these symmetries is also a symmetry of the whole prism.

It follows from the strategy that the number of symmetries of the triangular prism is $3 \times 4 = 12$.

5.3 (a) We consider a square face of the second type as the base—a square face with two edges that are joined to triangular faces and two to square faces. The small rhombicuboctahedron has 12 square faces of this type. Only 4 of the symmetries of this square base give symmetries of the rhombicuboctahedron.

It follows from Strategy 5.2 that the number of symmetries of the rhombicuboctahedron is $12 \times 4 = 48$.

(b) We consider a triangular face as the base. The small rhombicuboctahedron has 8 triangular faces. All 6 symmetries of this equilateral triangle base give symmetries of the polyhedron.

It follows from Strategy 5.2 that the number of symmetries of the polyhedron is $8 \times 6 = 48$.

(As expected, we obtain the same number of symmetries whichever face we consider.)

5.4 (a) Rectangular block

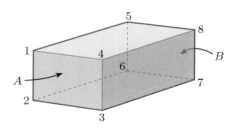

The rectangular block has six faces—three pairs of opposite faces. Opposite faces are congruent rectangles: if faces are not opposite each other, then they are not congruent.

1. Select the 2 congruent faces denoted by A and B in the above diagram.

2. Each of these faces is a rectangle, and so has four symmetries (since the order of $S(\square)$ is 4).

   Each of the symmetries is also a symmetry of the whole block.

It follows from Strategy 5.2 that the number of symmetries of the rectangular block is $2 \times 4 = 8$.

(b) There are two possible approaches here: we give the details of both.

First we list the symmetries which map A to A and B to B. (These are essentially the symmetries of a rectangle.)

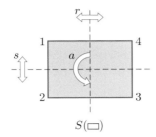

$$S(\square)$$

The two-line symbols for these symmetries are

$$e = \begin{pmatrix} 1 & 2 & 3 & 4 & 5 & 6 & 7 & 8 \\ 1 & 2 & 3 & 4 & 5 & 6 & 7 & 8 \end{pmatrix},$$

$$a = \begin{pmatrix} 1 & 2 & 3 & 4 & 5 & 6 & 7 & 8 \\ 3 & 4 & 1 & 2 & 7 & 8 & 5 & 6 \end{pmatrix},$$

$$r = \begin{pmatrix} 1 & 2 & 3 & 4 & 5 & 6 & 7 & 8 \\ 4 & 3 & 2 & 1 & 8 & 7 & 6 & 5 \end{pmatrix},$$

$$s = \begin{pmatrix} 1 & 2 & 3 & 4 & 5 & 6 & 7 & 8 \\ 2 & 1 & 4 & 3 & 6 & 5 & 8 & 7 \end{pmatrix}.$$

Now we consider the reflection w in the vertical plane shown below.

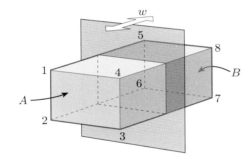

The reflection

$$w = \begin{pmatrix} 1 & 2 & 3 & 4 & 5 & 6 & 7 & 8 \\ 5 & 6 & 7 & 8 & 1 & 2 & 3 & 4 \end{pmatrix}$$

maps A to B and B to A, so we obtain the four remaining symmetries by composing each of the above symmetries with w on the right:

$$w = e \circ w = \begin{pmatrix} 1 & 2 & 3 & 4 & 5 & 6 & 7 & 8 \\ 5 & 6 & 7 & 8 & 1 & 2 & 3 & 4 \end{pmatrix},$$

$$x = a \circ w = \begin{pmatrix} 1 & 2 & 3 & 4 & 5 & 6 & 7 & 8 \\ 7 & 8 & 5 & 6 & 3 & 4 & 1 & 2 \end{pmatrix},$$

$$y = r \circ w = \begin{pmatrix} 1 & 2 & 3 & 4 & 5 & 6 & 7 & 8 \\ 8 & 7 & 6 & 5 & 4 & 3 & 2 & 1 \end{pmatrix},$$

$$z = s \circ w = \begin{pmatrix} 1 & 2 & 3 & 4 & 5 & 6 & 7 & 8 \\ 6 & 5 & 8 & 7 & 2 & 1 & 4 & 3 \end{pmatrix}.$$

Alternatively, we find first the direct symmetries and then the indirect symmetries, as in the video programme. The non-trivial direct symmetries a, y and z are anticlockwise rotations through π about the axes shown below.

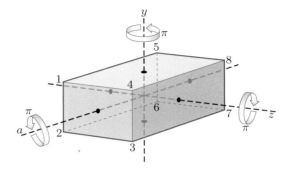

The two-line symbols for the direct symmetries are

$$e = \begin{pmatrix} 1 & 2 & 3 & 4 & 5 & 6 & 7 & 8 \\ 1 & 2 & 3 & 4 & 5 & 6 & 7 & 8 \end{pmatrix},$$

$$a = \begin{pmatrix} 1 & 2 & 3 & 4 & 5 & 6 & 7 & 8 \\ 3 & 4 & 1 & 2 & 7 & 8 & 5 & 6 \end{pmatrix},$$

$$y = \begin{pmatrix} 1 & 2 & 3 & 4 & 5 & 6 & 7 & 8 \\ 8 & 7 & 6 & 5 & 4 & 3 & 2 & 1 \end{pmatrix},$$

$$z = \begin{pmatrix} 1 & 2 & 3 & 4 & 5 & 6 & 7 & 8 \\ 6 & 5 & 8 & 7 & 2 & 1 & 4 & 3 \end{pmatrix}.$$

We obtain the four indirect symmetries by composing each of the direct symmetries with the indirect symmetry w (given above) on the right:

$$w = e \circ w = \begin{pmatrix} 1 & 2 & 3 & 4 & 5 & 6 & 7 & 8 \\ 5 & 6 & 7 & 8 & 1 & 2 & 3 & 4 \end{pmatrix},$$

$$x = a \circ w = \begin{pmatrix} 1 & 2 & 3 & 4 & 5 & 6 & 7 & 8 \\ 7 & 8 & 5 & 6 & 3 & 4 & 1 & 2 \end{pmatrix},$$

$$r = y \circ w = \begin{pmatrix} 1 & 2 & 3 & 4 & 5 & 6 & 7 & 8 \\ 4 & 3 & 2 & 1 & 8 & 7 & 6 & 5 \end{pmatrix},$$

$$s = z \circ w = \begin{pmatrix} 1 & 2 & 3 & 4 & 5 & 6 & 7 & 8 \\ 2 & 1 & 4 & 3 & 6 & 5 & 8 & 7 \end{pmatrix}.$$

Index